RISING STARS

Practice and homework

Year 5

This book is not photocopiable.

Rising Stars UK Ltd., 7 Hatchers Mews, Bermondsey Street,
London SE1 3GS

www.risingstars-uk.com

All facts are correct at time of going to press.

First published as *New Framework Maths Practice and Homework Year 5.*
This reissue published 2011.

Cover design: Richard Scott
Design and illustration: Redmoor Design, Tavistock, Devon
Editorial consultant: Ann Todd

British Library Cataloguing in Publication Data
A CIP record for this book is available from the British Library.

ISBN: 978-1-84680-945-3

Printed by Craft Print International Ltd., Singapore

Contents

Coverage of Primary Framework for mathematics

	Page number
Using and applying mathematics	
Solve one and two-step problems involving whole numbers and decimals and all four operations, choosing and using appropriate calculation strategies, including calculator use	21, 23, 58, 59
Represent a puzzle or problem by identifying and recording the information or calculations needed to solve it; find possible solutions and confirm them in the context of the problem	23
Plan and pursue an enquiry; present evidence by collecting, organising and interpreting information; suggest extensions to the enquiry	57
Explore patterns, properties and relationships and propose a general statement involving numbers or shapes; identify examples for which the statement is true or false	17
Explain reasoning using diagrams, graphs and text; refine ways of recording using images and symbols	63
Counting and understanding number	
Count from any given number in whole-number and decimal steps, extending beyond zero when counting backwards; relate the numbers to their position on a number line	8
Explain what each digit represents in whole numbers and decimals with up to two places, and partition, round and order these numbers	13, 14, 15
Express a smaller whole number as a fraction of a larger one (e.g. recognise that 5 out of 8 is $\frac{5}{8}$); find equivalent fractions (e.g. $\frac{7}{10} = \frac{14}{20}$, or $\frac{19}{10} = 1\frac{9}{10}$); relate fractions to their decimal representations	12
Understand percentage as the number of parts in every 100 and express tenths and hundredths as percentages	16
Use sequences to scale numbers up or down; solve problems involving proportions of quantities (e.g. decrease quantities in a recipe designed to feed six people)	
Knowing and using number facts	
Use knowledge of place value and addition and subtraction of two-digit numbers to derive sums and differences, and doubles and halves of decimals (e.g. 6.5 ± 2.7, half of 5.6, double 0.34)	18, 19
Recall quickly multiplication facts up to 10×10 and use them to multiply pairs of multiples of 10 and 100; derive quickly corresponding division facts	9
Identify pairs of factors of two-digit whole numbers and find common multiples (e.g. for 6 and 9)	10
Use knowledge of rounding, place value, number facts and inverse operations to estimate and check calculations	32
Calculating	
Extend mental methods for whole-number calculations, e.g. to multiply a two-digit by a one-digit number (e.g. 12×9), to multiply by 25 (e.g. 16×25), to subtract one near multiple of 1000 from another (e.g. $6070 - 4097$)	24, 25, 26

	Page number
Use efficient written methods to add and subtract whole numbers and decimals with up to two places	18, 19
Use understanding of place value to multiply and divide whole numbers and decimals by 10, 100 or 1000	26
Refine and use efficient written methods to multiply and divide HTU × U, TU × TU, U.t × U, and HTU ÷ U	20, 22, 27, 28, 29, 30
Find fractions using division (e.g. $\frac{1}{100}$ of 5 kg), and percentages of numbers and quantities (e.g. 10%, 5% and 15% of £80)	11
Use a calculator to solve problems, including those involving decimals or fractions (e.g. to find $\frac{3}{4}$ of 150 g); interpret the display correctly in the context of measurement	11, 31
Understanding shape	
Identify, visualise and describe properties of rectangles, triangles, regular polygons and 3D solids; use knowledge of properties to draw 2D shapes, and to identify and draw nets of 3D shapes	40, 41, 42, 43, 44, 45, 48, 49, 50, 51
Read and plot coordinates in the first quadrant; recognise parallel and perpendicular lines in grids and shapes; use a set-square and ruler to draw shapes with perpendicular or parallel sides	56
Complete patterns with up to two lines of symmetry; draw the position of a shape after a reflection or translation	46, 47
Estimate, draw and measure acute and obtuse angles using an angle measurer or protractor to a suitable degree of accuracy; calculate angles in a straight line	52, 53, 54, 55
Measuring	
Read, choose, use and record standard metric units to estimate and measure length, weight and capacity to a suitable degree of accuracy (e.g. the nearest centimetre); convert larger to smaller units using decimals to one place (e.g. change 2.6 kg to 2600 g)	33, 34, 35
Interpret a reading that lies between two unnumbered divisions on a scale	38
Draw and measure lines to the nearest millimetre; measure and calculate the perimeter of regular and irregular polygons; use the formula for the area of a rectangle to calculate the rectangle's area	36, 37
Read timetables and time using 24-hour clock notation; use a calendar to calculate time intervals	39
Handling data	
Describe the occurrence of familiar events using the language of chance or likelihood	64
Answer a set of related questions by collecting, selecting and organising relevant data; draw conclusions, using ICT to present features, and identify further questions to ask	60, 61, 62, 63
Construct frequency tables, pictograms and bar and line graphs to represent the frequencies of events and changes over time	63
Find and interpret the mode of a set of data	62, 63

How to use this book

New Medal Maths has been created to provide you with lots of practice to support your maths learning.

To make it more fun for you, the activities are organised around an Olympic Games theme including sporting topics, training tips and the bronze, silver and gold medals. The medals indicate three different levels of difficulty.

As Pierre de Coubertin, the founder of the Modern Olympic Games, said "The most important thing in the Olympic Games is not to win but to take part …"!

Practice and more practice is the best method for getting results and improving your performance in maths.

For the best results:

a) read the explanation;

b) complete the questions at the most appropriate level;

c) use the hints and tips to help you;

d) see if you can complete the next level of questions!

Explanations
Explanations and examples are given to support you working independently.

Bronze Medal Questions
These questions are an ideal starting point. They support the work covered in the Silver questions.

Silver Medal Questions
These questions are set at the expected level for Year 5 as presented by the Primary Framework.

Primary Framework for mathematics
Every objective is covered through an explanation, three levels of questions and hints and tips.

Rounding up or down

When using division in word problems, it is important to make sensible decisions about whether to round the answer up or down.

Examples

It costs £5 per person to get into the zoo. Jen has £32. How many people can Jen take into the zoo?

32 ÷ 5 = 6 r 2

We **round down** to 6 people.

A CD rack holds 20 CDs. How many CD racks do I need to hold 83 CDs?

83 ÷ 20 = 4 r 3 I need 5 CD racks.

We **round up** because 4 CD racks would leave 3 CDs.

Gold Medal Questions
These questions are a bit harder. They extend the work of the Silver questions.

a) Complete:

1. 63 ÷ 5 = (round up)
2. 41 ÷ 2 = (round down)
3. 32 ÷ 3 = (round up)

b) Complete:

1. A car carries 5 people. How many cars do we need to carry 24 people?
2. A CD rack holds 40 CDs. How many CD racks do we need to hold 74 CDs?
3. It costs £10 to get into the theme park. Sam has £95. How many people can Sam take to the theme park?

a) Complete:

1. 84 ÷ 9 = (round up)
2. 64 ÷ 6 = (round down)
3. 62 ÷ 5 = (round down)

b) Complete:

1. A van carries 3 people. How many vans do we need to carry 25 people?
2. A CD rack holds 9 CDs. How many CD racks do we need to hold 74 CDs?
3. It costs £7 to get into the theme park. Sam has £67. How many people can Sam take to the theme park?

a) Complete:

1. 40 ÷ 15 = (round up)
2. 108 ÷ 11 = (round down)
3. 75 ÷ 7 = (round down)

b) Complete:

1. A minibus carries 11 people. How many minibuses do we need to carry 60 people?
2. A CD rack holds 12 CDs. How many CD racks do we need to hold 75 CDs?
3. It costs £9 to get into the theme park. Sam has £85. How many people can Sam take to the theme park?

Questions
There are hundreds of questions covering all the content for the Primary Framework.

- Drawing pictures could help you to decide whether to round up or down.

Hints and Tips
Hints and tips to help you answer the questions.

Themes
Everyday situations, and a focus on sport, are used within the questions to put the maths into context.

Negative numbers

Numbers less than zero are called **negative numbers**.

To read these numbers we use the word **negative** or **minus**.

−8 is read as minus 8 or negative 8.

A number line can help when we add and subtract negative numbers.

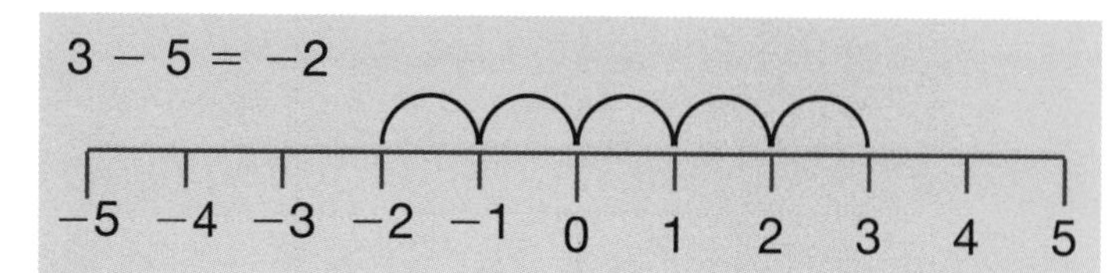

a) Write number lines into your book and fill in the missing numbers:

1. −5, □, □, −2, −1, 0, 1 □, 3, 4
2. □, −6, □, −2, 0, 2, 4, □, 8, □
3. −50, □, □, −20, −10, □, 10, □

b) Use a number line to order these numbers, smallest to largest:

1. 2, −4, −1, 8, 0
2. −8, 6, −2, −4, 9
3. 4, −4, 11, 6, 10

a) Finish these sequences:

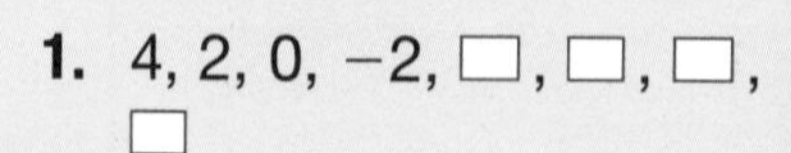

1. 4, 2, 0, −2, □, □, □, □
2. 8, 4, 0, −4, □, □, □, □
3. 10, 5, 0, □, □, □, □

b) Use the thermometer to work out the new temperature:

1. 4° − 6° = □°

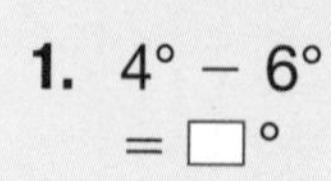

2. 2° − 8° = □°

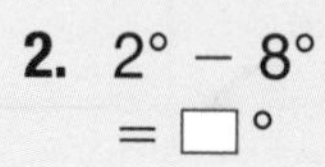

3. −5° + 7° = □°

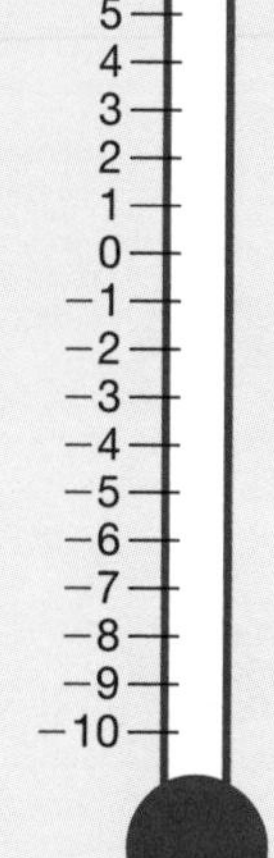

a) Order these numbers, smallest to largest:

1. −6, −180, −132, −200, 8
2. −600, −11, 8, 64, 0
3. −33, 30, −32, 0, −30

b) Answer these sums:

1. 12 − 30 =
2. 52 − 102 =
3. −36 + 48 =

c) Try these:

1. The temperature is 15°C. It drops 34°C. What is the new temperature?
2. The temperature is −8°C. It rises 12°C. What is the new temperature?

Training Tips

- **Make sure you remember to use the minus sign if the number is below zero.**

Square numbers

When you multiply a number by itself, the answer is called a **square number**.

Example

$3 \times 3 = 9$ so three squared = 9

They are called square numbers because they can be represented by dots in the form of a square.

A simple way to write the square of 3 is 3^2

The square of 3 is $3 \times 3 = 9$.
9 dots can form a square

a) Work out the following answers:

1. $2 \times 2 =$

2. $3 \times 3 =$

3. $4 \times 4 =$

b) Are these square numbers? Yes or no?

1. 4 **2.** 6 **3.** 14

c) One number in each list is a square number. Which one?

1. 14, 16, 18

2. 20, 25, 30

3. 0, 1, 3

a) Work out the following square numbers:

1. $2^2 = 2 \times 2 =$

2. $3^2 = 3 \times 3 =$

3. $4^2 = 4 \times 4 =$

b) Are these square numbers? Yes or no?

1. 10 **2.** 27 **3.** 25

c) One number in each list is a square number. Which one?

1. 8, 16, 12, 24, 20

2. 32, 60, 46, 64, 23

3. 65, 25, 10, 45, 50

a) Work out the following:

1. 5^2 **2.** 6^2 **3.** 7^2

b) One number in each list is a square number. Which one?

1. 29, 99, 90, 9, 89

2. 21, 7, 31, 14, 1

3. 83, 8, 81, 80, 88

- **A square number is a number multiplied by itself.**

Factors

A **factor** is a number that divides exactly into another number.

Example

$3 \times 5 = 15$ so 3 and 5 are both factors of 15

We list factors like this
Factors of 10: 1, 2, 5, 10

You can also look at the highest factor that two numbers share.
The highest factor shared by 10 and 15 is 5.

a) For which number are these the pairs of factors?

1. $1 \times 6, 2 \times 3$
2. 1×11
3. $1 \times 9, 3 \times 3$

b) Complete these pairs of factors:

1. 25: $1 \times 25, 5 \times \square$
2. 27: $1 \times \square, 3 \times 9$
3. 12: $1 \times 12, 2 \times \square, 3 \times 4$

c) Write the missing factors:

1. Factors of 12: 1 2 □ 4 6 12
2. Factors of 8: 1 2 □ 8
3. Factors of 4: □ 2 4

a) For which number are these the pairs of factors?

1. 1×37
2. $1 \times 15, 3 \times 5$
3. $1 \times 46, 2 \times 23$

b) Write all the pairs of factors for each number:

1. 10 **2.** 4 **3.** 16

c) List all of the factors of these numbers:

1. 6 **2.** 14 **3.** 26

a) Write the missing factors:

1. Factors of 28: 1 2 □ □ 14 28
2. Factors of 32: 1 2 □ □ 16 32
3. Factors of 34: 1 □ 17 □

b) List all the factors of these numbers:

1. 40 **2.** 54 **3.** 13

c) Write the highest factor common to these numbers:

1. 25 and 35
2. 12 and 16
3. 14 and 21

- **Think of factors as pairs of numbers whose product is the target number.**

Fractions of amounts

$\frac{1}{4}$ of 16 is the same as $16 \div 4 = 4$

Example
What is $\frac{1}{5}$ of £25?
$25 \div 5 = 5$ so $\frac{1}{5}$ of £25 = £5

a) Find $\frac{1}{2}$ of:

1. 8

2. 20

3. 16

b) Find $\frac{1}{10}$ of:

1. 20

2. 80

3. 10

c) Find $\frac{1}{5}$ of:

1. 45

2. 25

3. 50

a) Find:

1. $\frac{1}{10}$ of 80

2. $\frac{1}{5}$ of 45

3. $\frac{1}{8}$ of 16

b) Complete:

1. $\frac{1}{5}$ of 20 = 4
$\frac{2}{5}$ of 20 = ☐

2. $\frac{1}{4}$ of 12 = ☐
$\frac{2}{4}$ of 12 = ☐

3. $\frac{1}{10}$ of 60 = ☐
$\frac{3}{10}$ of 60 = ☐

c) Find:

1. $\frac{2}{3}$ of 75p

2. $\frac{3}{5}$ of 25 m

3. $\frac{6}{8}$ of £56

a) Complete:

1. $\frac{1}{10}$ of 80 = ☐
$\frac{6}{10}$ of 80 = ☐

2. $\frac{1}{7}$ of 35 = ☐
$\frac{5}{7}$ of 35 = ☐

3. $\frac{1}{8}$ of 24 = ☐
$\frac{3}{8}$ of 24 = ☐

b) Find:

1. $\frac{4}{6}$ of 30

2. $\frac{5}{8}$ of 56

3. $\frac{9}{11}$ of 110

c) Find:

1. $\frac{7}{10}$ of 120 cm

2. $\frac{2}{5}$ of 1 litre

3. $\frac{6}{10}$ of 1 m

- **Divide by the denominator and multiply by the numerator.**

Equivalent fractions

Looking at these diagrams you can see that the same area is shaded. So if $\frac{1}{4}$ is coloured, it is the same as $\frac{2}{8}$. We say $\frac{1}{4}$ is equivalent to $\frac{2}{8}$.

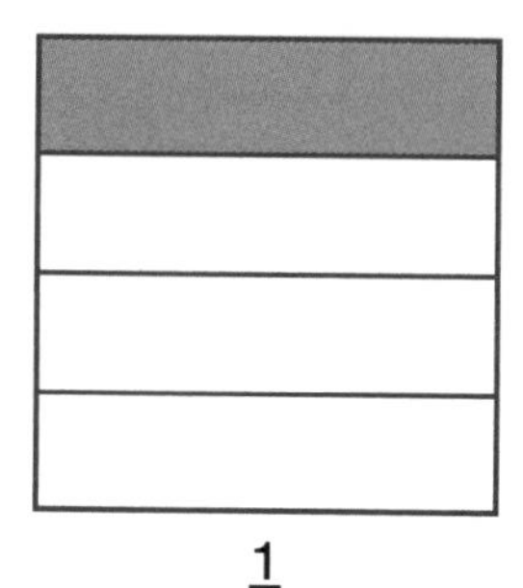

$\frac{1}{4}$

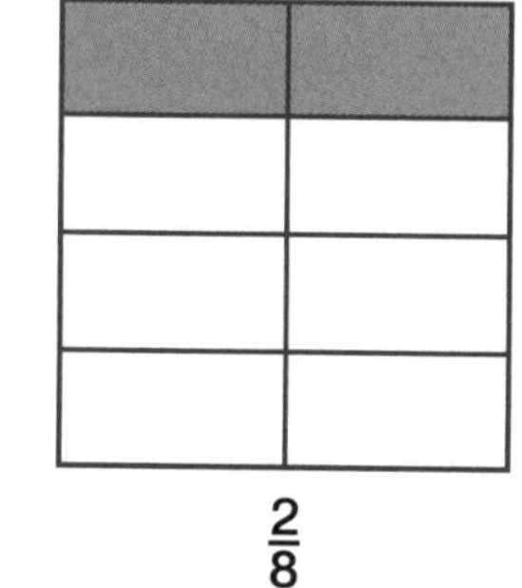

$\frac{2}{8}$

You can make equivalent fractions by multiplying or dividing the numerator and denominator by the same number.

Multiplying

$$\frac{1}{4}\,\frac{(\times 2)}{(\times 2)} = \frac{2}{8}\,\frac{(\times 2)}{(\times 2)} = \frac{4}{16}$$

Dividing

$$\frac{9}{27}\,\frac{(\div 3)}{(\div 3)} = \frac{3}{9}\,\frac{(\div 3)}{(\div 3)} = \frac{1}{3}$$

a) Complete:

1. $\frac{1}{2}\,\frac{(\times 2)}{(\times 2)} = \frac{}{4}$
2. $\frac{1}{3}\,\frac{(\times 2)}{(\times 2)} = \frac{}{6}$
3. $\frac{3}{5}\,\frac{(\times 3)}{(\times 3)} = \frac{}{15}$

b) Match the fractions to their equivalents:

1. $\frac{1}{2}$ $\qquad$ $\frac{3}{18}$
2. $\frac{1}{6}$ $\qquad$ $\frac{3}{12}$
3. $\frac{1}{4}$ $\qquad$ $\frac{3}{6}$

a) Complete:

1. $\frac{2}{6}\,\frac{(\times 3)}{(\times 3)} = \frac{}{18}$
2. $\frac{4}{5}\,\frac{(\times 4)}{(\times 4)} = \frac{}{20}$
3. $\frac{2}{3}\,\frac{(\times 6)}{(\times 6)} = \frac{}{18}$

b) Match the fractions to their equivalents:

1. $\frac{3}{4}$ $\qquad$ $\frac{36}{45}$
2. $\frac{4}{5}$ $\qquad$ $\frac{80}{100}$
3. $\frac{8}{10}$ $\qquad$ $\frac{9}{12}$

a) Complete:

1. $\frac{11}{13} = \frac{22}{}$
2. $\frac{9}{15} = \frac{}{30}$
3. $\frac{7}{10} = \frac{}{1000}$

b) Match the fractions to their equivalents:

1. $\frac{10}{14}$ $\qquad$ $\frac{36}{81}$
2. $\frac{6}{10}$ $\qquad$ $\frac{600}{1000}$
3. $\frac{4}{9}$ $\qquad$ $\frac{20}{28}$

- **Fractions where the numerator and denominator are the same = 1.**

Decimal fractions

Decimals are another way of writing fractions.

The fraction $\frac{13}{100}$ can be written as 0.13.

The 1 equals $\frac{10}{100}$ and the 3 equals $\frac{3}{100}$.

Look at this table for 3.675:

3	. 6	7	5
3 units	. 6 tenths	7 hundredths	5 thousandths
3 units	. $\frac{6}{10}$	$\frac{7}{100}$	$\frac{5}{1000}$

a) **Write these in words:**

1. 0.2 = Nought point
2. 0.8 = Nought point
3. 6.2 = Six point

b) **Write these in figures:**

1. Nought point three
2. Three point four
3. Nine point six

c) **Partition these numbers:**

1. 8.4 = 8 + □
2. 9.2 = □ + 0.2
3. 6.7 = 6 + □

a) **Write the decimal fraction that is the same as the following:**

1. Three tenths and four hundredths
2. Forty-six tenths and seven hundredths
3. Nine and nine hundredths

b) **What does the digit in blue represent?**

1. 6.25
2. 9.24
3. 1.62

c) **Partition these decimals:**

1. 7.23 = □ + 0.2 + □
2. 4.98 = 4 + □ + □
3. 8.32 = □ + □ + 0.02

a) **Write the decimal fraction that is the same as the following:**

1. Forty-six tenths, three hundredths and seven thousandths
2. Nine and nine thousandths
3. Twenty-one, five hundredths and three thousandths

b) **What does the digit in blue represent?**

1. 6.235
2. 9.524
3. 1.962

- **Read a decimal out loud. 3.6 is 'three point six'.**

Ordering decimals

When ordering decimals, remember to line up each decimal in a column and make sure they have the same number of digits.

Always read numbers from left to right and compare.

a) Copy the number line. Put each number below on the number line.

1. 1

2. 0.5

3. 0.9

b) Which is bigger?

1. 1.9 or 9.2

2. 8.0 or 0.8

3. 6.2 or 62

c) Order these decimals, smallest to largest:

1. 6.3, 1.7, 9.7

2. 7.8, 2.4, 4.1

3. 6.2, 8.5, 1.3

0.1 0.2 0.3

a) Copy the number line. Put each number below on the number line.

1. 0.2

2. 0.15

3. 0.19

b) Which is bigger?

1. 2.35 or 2.54

2. 3.67 or 36.7

3. 2.89 or 2.73

c) Write these measurements in order – smallest to largest:

1. 1.24 m, 2.41 m, 4.12 m, 1.42 m

2. 6.69 m, 9.66 m, 6.66 m, 6.99 m

3. 2.31 m, 1.32 m, 2.13 m, 1.23 m

a) Copy the number line. Put each number below on the number line.

1. 2.85

2. 2.81

3. 2.815

b) Which is bigger?

1. 3.456 or 3.487

2. 87.94 or 8.794

3. 9.532 or 9.542

c) Write these decimals in order – smallest first:

1. 8.778, 7.778, 7.787, 8.887

2. 5.664, 6.446, 6.554, 4.455

3. 7.967, 7.667, 7.776, 6.777

- **If you are ordering numbers with two decimal places, put in the zeros to help.**

Rounding decimals

Look at this number line. It is divided into tenths. The arrow is pointing to 1.6

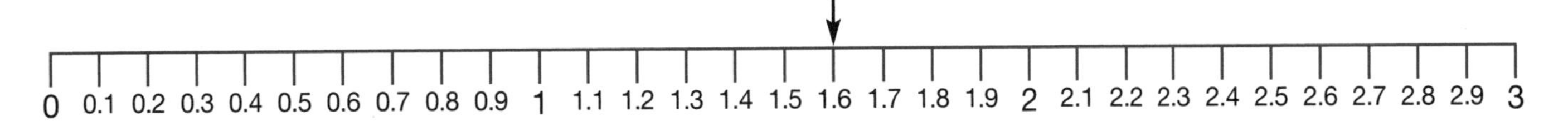

We say 1.6 rounded to the nearest whole number is 2.

a) For each arrow write which number it is pointing to and its nearest whole number.

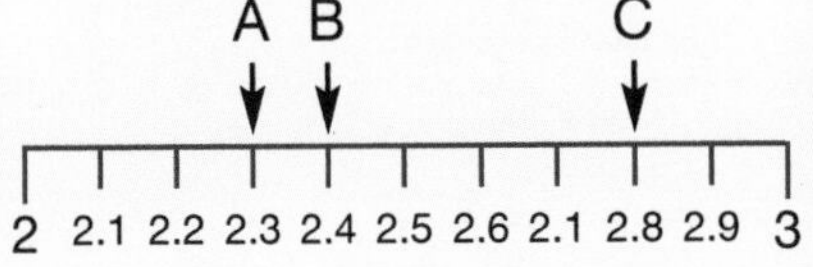

1. A = **2.** B = **3.** C =

b) Round these to the nearest whole number:

1. 2.2

2. 6.9

3. 8.6

c) Round these to the nearest pound:

1. £3.68

2. £6.41

3. £19.58

a) For each arrow write which number it is pointing to and its nearest whole number.

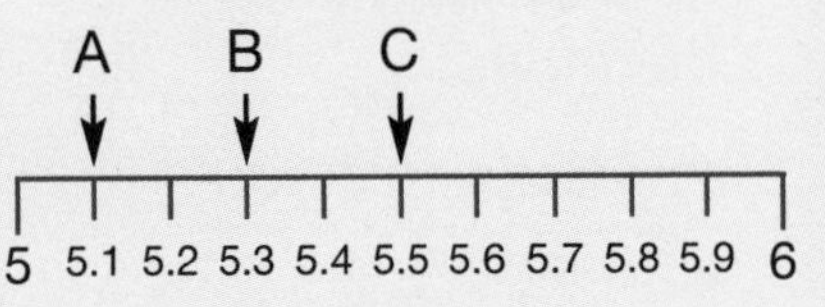

1. A = **2.** B = **3.** C =

b) Round these to the nearest whole number:

1. 2.52

2. 6.89

3. 8.56

c) Round these to the nearest ten pence:

1. £3.68

2. £6.41

3. £19.58

a) For each arrow write which number it is pointing to and its nearest whole number.

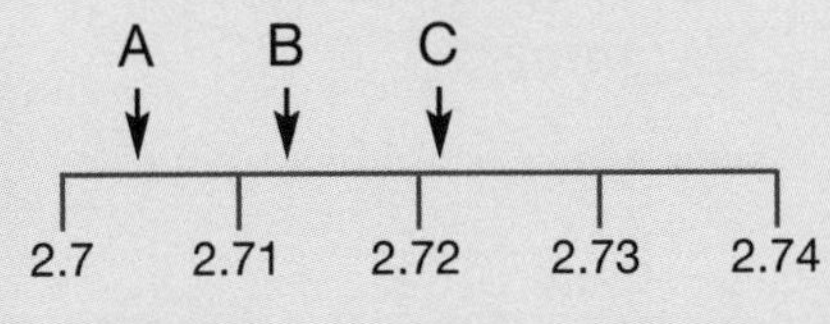

1. A = **2.** B = **3.** C =

b) Round these to the nearest tenth:

1. 8.814

2. 2.845

3. 6.062

c) Round these to the nearest hundredth:

1. 7.666

2. 0.235

3. 0.474

- **Use number lines to help.**

Percentages

Percentage means the number of parts in 100.

Every percentage has a decimal and a fraction equivalent.

56% = 56 out of 100 = $\frac{56}{100}$ = 0.56

Finding **percentages** of whole numbers is very similar to finding fractions of numbers.

If you are asked to find 10% of 50 then first find the fraction equivalent to 10%, which is $\frac{1}{10}$.

So the question now is to find $\frac{1}{10}$ of 50 = 50 ÷ 10 = 5. So 10% of 50 = 5.

Once you have found 10% you can find most other percentages by multiplying or dividing.

a) Write these percentages as fractions and decimals:

1. 34% = $\frac{\ }{100}$ = 0.34

2. 93% = $\frac{\ }{100}$ = $\square$

3. 56% = $\frac{\ }{100}$ = $\square$

4. 72% = $\frac{\ }{100}$ = $\square$

5. 85% = $\frac{\ }{100}$ = $\square$

b) Find 10% of:

1. 60 **2.** 20 **3.** 70

4. 80 **5.** 200

c) Find 50% of:

1. 10 **2.** 8 **3.** 16

4. 22 **5.** 48

a) Write these percentages as fractions and decimals:

1. 78% **2.** 39%

3. 83% **4.** 15%

5. 9%

b) Find 20% of:

1. 40 **2.** 100 **3.** 150

4. 90 **5.** 470

c) Work out:

1. 50% of 34

2. 30% of 120

3. 10% of £1.80

4. 40% of £3.20

5. 5% of £6.70

a) Write each fraction as a decimal and a percentage:

1. $\frac{67}{100}$ **2.** $\frac{5}{10}$ **3.** $\frac{1}{5}$

b) Write each decimal as a fraction and a percentage:

1. 0.98 **2.** 0.05

3. 0.75 **4.** 0.4

c) Find 75% of:

1. 12p **2.** 24p **3.** £100

d) Find these amounts:

1. 40% of £50

2. 45% of £80

3. 55% of £120

- **Change fractions into hundredths to find percentages.**

Ratio and proportion

Ratio is used to make comparisons.

In this pattern for every 1 square there are 2 circles.

If I add another square, I will need to add 2 circles to keep the ratio the same.

We say the ratio of squares to circles is 1:2

Proportion is also used to compare amounts.

For the above picture:

- the proportion of squares is $\frac{1}{3}$
- the proportion of circles is $\frac{2}{3}$

Copy and complete:

1. In a row of 12 tiles with every third one white, there are ☐ blue tiles for every ☐ white tile.
2. In a row of 12 tiles with the pattern reversed, there are ☐ blue tiles for every ☐ white tile.
3. In a row of 16 tiles with 3 blue then 1 white tile, there are ☐ blue tiles for every ☐ white tile.
4. A pattern has red and blue tiles. The proportion of red to blue is 1 in every 4 tiles. Draw the pattern with 12 tiles altogether.

Copy and complete:

1. In a row of 15 tiles with every fifth one white, there are ☐ blue tiles for every ☐ white tile.
2. In a row of 15 tiles with the ratio 3:2, there are ☐ blue tiles for every ☐ white tile.
3. A pattern of blue and red tiles has 1 blue tile for every 2 red tiles. Draw a pattern to match this statement. What is the proportion of tiles in the pattern?

Copy and complete:

1. In a row of 24 tiles with the ratio 3:5, there are ☐ blue tiles for every ☐ white tile.
2. In a row of 18 tiles with the ratio 3:6, there are ☐ blue tiles for every ☐ white tile.
3. Draw the pattern to match the statement: a pattern of yellow and green tiles has 1 green for every yellow. What is the ratio? What is the proportion?
4. At the athletics club, there are 3 boys for every 2 girls. There are 40 children at the club. How many boys are there?
5. If the ratio stayed the same, how many girls would there be if the membership of the club increased to 60?

- **You can simplify ratios by dividing each side by the same number.**

Adding decimals

Adding decimals is exactly the same as adding other numbers. You can still use the method you would normally use.

Solve these:

1. 2.4 + 3.3 =
2. 1.3 + 2.4 =
3. 3.2 + 2.5 =
4. 1.7 + 7.2 =
5. 1.5 + 5.2 =
6. 7.4 + 2.3 =
7. 5.1 + 3.7 =
8. 6.4 + 2.5 =
9. 4.4 + 5.3 =
10. 3.4 + 1.9 =
11. £7.20 + £1.50 =
12. £2.30 + £4.60 =

Solve these:

1. 7.64 + 2.25 =
2. 2.91 + 4.04 =
3. 1.17 + 6.17 =
4. 3.22 + 5.27 =
5. 0.62 + 1.12 =
6. 2.28 + 4.63 =
7. 1.64 + 6.28 =
8. 5.14 + 2.56 =
9. 3.68 + 2.17 =
10. 6.24 + 2.19 =
11. £5.44 + £2.94 =
12. £6.62 + £3.60 =

Solve these:

1. 7.44 + 2.71 =
2. 3.84 + 4.33 =
3. 3.52 + 4.63 =
4. 5.61 + 1.54 =
5. 4.83 + 1.95 =
6. 2.66 + 3.75 =
7. 6.97 + 1.45 =
8. 2.74 + 3.47 =
9. 1.86 + 6.35 =
10. 4.82 + 1.49 =
11. £2.75 + £3.47 =
12. £5.93 + £3.28 =

- When adding decimals, make sure the numbers are in the correct column so that the decimal points line up.

Subtracting decimals

Subtracting decimals is exactly the same as subtracting other numbers. You can still use the method you would normally use.

Solve these:

1. 9.9 − 7.2 =
2. 1.8 − 1.3 =
3. 6.8 − 4.3 =
4. 5.7 − 2.4 =
5. 4.7 − 2.4 =
6. 2.6 − 1.3 =
7. 7.4 − 4.3 =
8. 3.6 − 1.5 =
9. 4.6 − 2.6 =
10. 2.9 − 1.6 =
11. £6.58 − £3.25 =
12. £8.47 − £5.14 =

Solve these:

1. 5.64 − 2.21 =
2. 6.47 − 4.15 =
3. 4.39 − 1.17 =
4. 6.94 − 5.22 =
5. 9.74 − 6.43 =
6. 2.94 − 1.77 =
7. 6.83 − 3.57 =
8. 3.36 − 1.55 =
9. 3.71 − 2.38 =
10. 8.38 − 2.47 =
11. £7.64 − £6.39 =
12. £2.44 − £1.63 =

Solve these:

1. 7.63 − 4.07 =
2. 2.50 − 1.04 =
3. 7.21 − 6.02 =
4. 8.76 − 7.59 =
5. 7.97 − 4.89 =
6. 2.37 − 1.79 =
7. 6.54 − 2.68 =
8. 5.20 − 1.78 =
9. 5.41 − 2.54 =
10. 4.15 − 1.89 =
11. £6.06 − £4.77 =
12. £7.31 − £3.57 =

- **Watch out for subtraction traps!**

Understanding multiplication and division

If you know $3 \times 6 = 18$, then you also know the following:

$6 \times 3 = 18$ $18 \div 6 = 3$ $18 \div 3 = 6$

You are going to practise finding these related facts on this page.

For each given statement, complete three other related facts.

$5 \times 7 = 35$

1. $\square \times 5 = \square$
2. $35 \div \square = 7$
3. $35 \div \square = \square$

$8 \times 9 = 72$

4. $\square \times \square = 72$
5. $72 \div \square = \square$
6. $72 \div \square = \square$

$24 \div 6 = 4$

7. $24 \div \square = 6$
8. $6 \times \square = \square$
9. $\square \times \square = 24$

$27 \div 3 = 9$

10. $27 \div \square = \square$
11. $3 \times \square = \square$
12. $\square \times 3 = \square$

a) For each of these statements, write the three related facts.

1. $6 \times 9 = 54$
2. $56 \div 7 = 8$
3. $12 \times 2 = 24$

b) Complete these statements and write the three related facts.

1. $5 \times 6 =$
2. $7 \times 9 =$
3. $24 \div 2 =$

c) Copy and complete:

1. $2 \times \square = 36$
2. $\square \times 9 = 27$
3. $36 \div \square = 6$

a) Complete these statements and write the three related facts.

1. $3 \times 7 =$
2. $9 \times 8 =$
3. $5 \times 9 =$

b) Write four statements for each set of numbers.

1. 20, 8, 160
2. 90, 6, 15
3. 28, 4, 112

c) Copy and complete:

1. $15 \times \square = 135$
2. $\square \times 9 = 63$
3. $\square \div 6 = 20$

- **Always remember that multiplication is the opposite of division.**

Brackets

Brackets are very useful when you have a sum with more than one step.

We put brackets around the part of the sum that needs to be done first.

Example

$20 - (3 \times 6) = 20 - 18 = 2$

We solved the brackets first, then the rest of the sum.

a) Solve:

1. $10 + (2\times2) =$
2. $10 - (3\times2) =$
3. $10 - (4\times2) =$

b) Solve:

1. $(2\times10) + 8 =$
2. $(6\times5) - 20 =$
3. $(4\times2) + 6 =$

c) True or false?

1. $3 + (5\times3) = 18$
2. $4 + (9\times2) = 20$
3. $(2\times3) + 8 = 14$

a) Work out:

1. $10 \times (21-4) =$
2. $(3\times6) + 17 =$
3. $8 \times (2+3) =$

b) Solve:

1. $(24\div2) + 25 =$
2. $(66\div11) \times 5 =$
3. $100 - (54\div9) =$

c) True or false?

1. $(2\times3) + (3\times5) = 20$
2. $(8\times7) - (4\times2) = 48$
3. $(36\div9) + (2\times5) = 15$

Gold

a) Solve:

1. $2 \times (5+7+8) =$
2. $10 \times (9+8+7+6) =$
3. $5 \times (9-7+4) =$

b) Work out:

1. $(42\div7) + 11 =$
2. $20 + (144\div12) =$
3. $(8\times7) + 35 =$

c) Solve:

1. $(3\times6) + (4\times2) =$
2. $(5\times8) + (3\times9) =$
3. $(9\times9) - (3\times6) =$

- Try to use brackets in your work when you use more than one operation.

Remainders

When we divide one number by another it can either divide exactly or leave **remainders**.

Example

25 ÷ 5 = 5.
There are no remainders.

But 25 ÷ 4 = 6 remainder 1.
That means 4 goes into 25 six times with 1 left over.

a) Match the answer for each sum to its remainder equivalent:

1. 45 ÷ 10 = 4 r 5 — $4\frac{2}{5}$
2. 22 ÷ 5 = 4 r 2 — 5.5
3. 11 ÷ 2 = 5 r 1 — $4\frac{1}{2}$

b) Give the remainder as a fraction:

1. 13 ÷ 2 =
2. 27 ÷ 5 =
3. 33 ÷ 2 =

c) Give the remainder as a decimal:

1. £46 ÷ 5 =
2. £25 ÷ 2 =
3. £86 ÷ 10 =

a) Give the remainder as a fraction:

1. 18 ÷ 4 =
2. 78 ÷ 5 =
3. 51 ÷ 8 =

b) Give the remainder as a decimal:

1. £164 ÷ 5 =
2. £490 ÷ 10 =
3. £6.30 ÷ 2 =

c) Give the remainder as a fraction and as a decimal:

1. 82 ÷ 4 =
2. 124 ÷ 10 =
3. 107 ÷ 5 =

a) Give the remainder as a fraction:

1. 174 ÷ 9 =
2. 163 ÷ 8 =
3. 135 ÷ 11 =

b) Give the remainder as a decimal:

1. £12.30 ÷ 5 =
2. £45.60 ÷ 4 =
3. £68.30 ÷ 2 =

c) Give the remainder as a fraction and as a decimal:

1. 95 ÷ 4 =
2. 1563 ÷ 10 =
3. 4576 ÷ 5 =

- **Look out for these division words: divide, remainder, quotient, share, divisible by.**

Rounding up or down

When using division in word problems, it is important to make sensible decisions about whether to round the answer up or down.

Examples

It costs £5 per person to get into the zoo. Jen has £32. How many people can Jen take into the zoo?

$32 \div 5 = 6 \text{ r } 2$

We **round down** to 6 people.

A CD rack holds 20 CDs. How many CD racks do I need to hold 83 CDs?

$83 \div 20 = 4 \text{ r } 3$ I need 5 CD racks.

We **round up** because 4 CD racks would leave 3 CDs.

a) Complete:

1. $63 \div 5 =$ (round up)
2. $41 \div 2 =$ (round down)
3. $32 \div 3 =$ (round up)

b) Complete:

1. A car carries 5 people. How many cars do we need to carry 24 people?
2. A CD rack holds 40 CDs. How many CD racks do we need to hold 74 CDs?
3. It costs £10 to get into the theme park. Sam has £95. How many people can Sam take to the theme park?

a) Complete:

1. $84 \div 9 =$ (round up)
2. $64 \div 6 =$ (round down)
3. $62 \div 5 =$ (round down)

b) Complete:

1. A van carries 3 people. How many vans do we need to carry 25 people?
2. A CD rack holds 9 CDs. How many CD racks do we need to hold 74 CDs?
3. It costs £7 to get into the theme park. Sam has £67. How many people can Sam take to the theme park?

a) Complete:

1. $40 \div 15 =$ (round up)
2. $108 \div 11 =$ (round down)
3. $75 \div 7 =$ (round down)

b) Complete:

1. A minibus carries 11 people. How many minibuses do we need to carry 60 people?
2. A CD rack holds 12 CDs. How many CD racks do we need to hold 75 CDs?
3. It costs £9 to get into the theme park. Sam has £85. How many people can Sam take to the theme park?

- **Drawing pictures could help you to decide whether to round up or down.**

Mental strategies

1. Using factors

Example

Look at the sum and find factors

$16 \times 5 = \mathbf{(2 \times 8)} \times 5$

Rearrange the sum to make it easier

$= 2 \times \mathbf{(8 \times 5)}$

$= 2 \times 40$

$= 80$

2. Multiplying by 19 or 21

To multiply by 19 or 21 we multiply by 20 and then adjust.

Example

$12 \times 19 = (12 \times 20) - (12 \times 1)$

$= 240 - 12$

$= 228$

a) Use factors to solve:

1. $7 \times 8 = 7 \times (\square \times 2) = (7 \times \square) \times 2 = \square$
2. $12 \times 6 = 12 \times (\square \times 2) = (12 \times \square) \times 2 = \square$
3. $12 \times 8 = \square$

b) Use factors to solve:

1. $64 \div 8 = 64 \div (2 \times \square) = (64 \div 2) \div \square = \square$
2. $48 \div 6 = 48 \div (2 \times \square) = (48 \div 2) \div \square = \square$
3. $72 \div 8 = \square$

a) Use factors to solve:

1. $15 \times 8 =$
2. $17 \times 6 =$
3. $16 \times 12 =$

b) Use factors to solve:

1. $104 \div 8 =$
2. $84 \div 6 =$
3. $132 \div 12 =$

c) Work out:

1. $16 \times 19 =$
2. $12 \times 19 =$
3. $18 \times 21 =$

a) Use factors to solve:

1. $13 \times 12 =$
2. $16 \times 21 =$
3. $14 \times 18 =$

b) Use factors to solve:

1. $168 \div 12 =$
2. $273 \div 21 =$
3. $288 \div 18 =$

c) Work out:

1. $12 \times 39 =$
2. $15 \times 29 =$
3. $16 \times 41 =$

- **Factors are pairs of numbers that can be multiplied together to reach your target.**

Mental strategies

1. Partitioning

Partitioning can be used for multiplication too!

Example

$12 \times 7 = (10 \times 7) + (2 \times 7)$
$= 70 + 14 = 84$

2. Adding

You can create a new times table by adding together two tables you already know!

Example

$2 \times 12 = 2 \times 10 + 2 \times 2 = 24$

a) Copy and complete:

1. $14 \times 3 =$
   $(10\times3) + (4\times3) =$
2. $16 \times 5 =$
   $(10\times5) + (6\times5) =$
3. $23 \times 4 =$
   $(20\times4) + (3\times4) =$

b) Complete this table to create the 16 times table:

×10	×6	×16
10	6	16
20	12	32
30	☐	☐
☐	24	☐
50	☐	80
☐	36	☐
☐	☐	112
☐	48	☐
90	☐	☐
☐	60	☐

a) Work out:

1. $18 \times 6 =$
   $(10\times6) + (8\times6) =$
2. $19 \times 8 =$
   $(10\times3) + (9\times8) =$
3. $27 \times 7 =$

b) Complete this table to create the 18 times table:

×8	×10	×18
8	10	18
16	20	36
☐	☐	☐
☐	☐	☐
40	☐	☐
☐	☐	☐
☐	☐	☐
64	☐	☐
☐	☐	☐
80	☐	☐

a) Work out:

1. $49 \times 7 =$
2. $3.2 \times 6 =$
3. $6.7 \times 9 =$

b) Complete this table to create the 23 times table:

×13	×10	×23
13	10	23
26	20	46

- **Remember × 10 – each digit moves one place to the left.**

Mental strategies

Place value

You can solve multiplication and division questions by using your knowledge of place value and your times tables.

If you know	$3 \times 6 = 18$
Then you also know	$3 \times 60 = 180$
And...	$3 \times 600 = 1800$

a) Copy and complete:

1. $4 \times 8 = 32$ $4 \times 80 =$
2. $3 \times 9 = 27$ $3 \times 90 =$
3. $6 \times 7 = 42$ $6 \times 70 =$

b) Match the sums with the answers:

1. $16 \times 10 =$ 120
2. $8 \times 50 =$ 400
3. $4 \times 30 =$ 160

c) Complete:

1. $6 \times 40 =$
2. $5 \times 30 =$
3. $3 \times 70 =$

a) Copy and complete:

1. $6 \times 8 =$
   $6 \times 80 =$
   $6 \times 800 =$
2. $7 \times 9 =$
   $7 \times 90 =$
   $7 \times 900 =$
3. $5 \times 7 =$
   $5 \times 70 =$
   $5 \times 700 =$

b) Work out:

1. $7 \times 80 =$
2. $4 \times 70 =$
3. $9 \times 600 =$

c) Work out:

1. $180 \div 20 =$
2. $5500 \div 50 =$
3. $2700 \div 300 =$

a) Work out:

1. $9 \times 30 =$
2. $8 \times 70 =$
3. $11 \times 600 =$

b) Work out:

1. $5600 \div 70 =$
2. $1800 \div 60 =$
3. $4000 \div 800 =$

c) Solve:

1. $\square \times 90 = 81000$
2. $1.5 \times \square = 3$
3. $7200 \div \square = 90$

- **When you multiply by 10 each digit moves one place to the left.**
- **When you divide by 10 each digit moves one place to the right.**

The chunking method

One way of dividing is to think of it as **repeated subtraction**.

For example, 329 ÷ 6 =

Think what large 'chunk' of 6s we can take away.

329
300 − (50 × 6)
29
24 − (4 × 6)
5

You cannot take away any more 6s as the number is less than 6.

So 6 goes into 329 fifty-four times (add the numbers in blue) with remainder 5.

a) **Copy and complete:**

1. 33 ÷ 3 =
33 − (**10** × 3)
3 − (**1** × 3)
0
Answer:

2. 65 ÷ 4 =

3. 75 ÷ 3 =

4. 63 ÷ 2 =

b) **Now practise the method with these sums:**

1. 85 ÷ 4 =

2. 62 ÷ 4 =

3. 46 ÷ 2 =

4. 34 ÷ 9 =

Using the chunking method, solve these:

1. 535 ÷ 6 =

2. 272 ÷ 5 =

3. 173 ÷ 4 =

4. 353 ÷ 3 =

5. 787 ÷ 8 =

6. 943 ÷ 5 =

7. 512 ÷ 9 =

8. 709 ÷ 7 =

Using the chunking method, solve these:

1. 6547 ÷ 6 =

2. 2795 ÷ 7 =

3. 3473 ÷ 4 =

4. 3578 ÷ 5 =

5. 8544 ÷ 3 =

6. 233 ÷ 13 =

7. 389 ÷ 26 =

8. 234 ÷ 18 =

- **Try to think of the biggest 'chunk' you can take away.**

Long multiplication

The standard method for multiplication is called long multiplication.
It is very similar to the grid method – you still need to partition – but it is set out differently.

Look at these two examples:

1.

$$\begin{array}{rl} 34 & \\ \times\ 18 & \\ \hline 340 & (34 \times 10) \\ 272 & (34 \times 8) \\ \hline 612 & \end{array}$$

2.

$$\begin{array}{rl} 22 & \\ \times\ 45 & \\ \hline 880 & (22 \times 40) \\ 110 & (22 \times 5) \\ \hline 990 & \end{array}$$

a) Copy and complete:

1. 6 × 12
(6 × 10)
(6 × 2)
___

2. 4 × 13
(4 × 10)
(4 × 3)
___

b) Work out:

1. 3 × 13 =

2. 6 × 15 =

3. 4 × 16 =

4. 5 × 14 =

5. 9 × 12 =

6. 3 × 18 =

a) Copy and complete:

1. 24 × 12
(24 × 10)
(24 × 2)
___

2. 17 × 13
(17 × 10)
(17 × 3)
___

b) Work out:

1. 53 ×11 **2.** 19 ×16

3. 23 ×18 **4.** 25 ×32

5. 41 ×24 **6.** 52 ×43

a) Copy and complete:

1. 324 × 12
(324 × 10)
(324 × 2)
___

2. 517 × 13
(517 × 10)
(517 × 3)
___

b) Work out:

1. 523 ×11 **2.** 189 ×16

3. 283 ×18 **4.** 225 ×32

5. 461 ×24 **6.** 582 ×43

- **As you gain confidence with this method, you don't need to write the sums in the brackets.**

Multiplying decimals

You can use any written method for multiplication when you are multiplying decimals.

You may want to use partitioning.

Example

$5.3 \times 6 = (5 \times 6) + (0.3 \times 6)$
$= 30 + 1.8$
$= 31.8$

a) Multiply by 2:

1. 1.2

2. 2.1

3. 2.6

b) Multiply by 3:

1. 2.3

2. 1.6

3. 4.2

c) Multiply by 10:

1. 4.8

2. 5.9

3. 2.5

a) Multiply by 4:

1. 4.6

2. 3.8

3. 6.2

b) Multiply by 5:

1. 7.4

2. 8.2

3. 4.8

c) Multiply by 100:

1. 3.7

2. 4.2

3. 12.8

a) Multiply by 2:

1. 1.34

2. 4.26

3. 7.54

b) Multiply by 3:

1. 1.42

2. 3.25

3. 4.37

c) Write the missing number:

1. $1.23 \times \square = 2.46$

2. $5.23 \times \square = 15.69$

3. $7.11 \times \square = 63.99$

- **Check your answer by adding. ($3.4 \times 3 = 3.4 + 3.4 + 3.4 = 10.2$)**

Short division

The standard method for division is called short division.

It uses a sign like this $\overline{)\quad}$ to mean divide.

You can solve this in the same way as short division – see Example 1.

Your teacher may teach you a different way to solve it – see Example 2.

Example 1

$3\overline{)145}$
-120 (40×3)
25
$-\ 24$ (8×3)
1

Answer 48 r 1

Example 2

48 r 1
$3\overline{)145}$
12
25
24
1

Answer 48 r 1

a) **Practise using short division by answering these questions:**

1. $2\overline{)428} =$
2. $3\overline{)369} =$
3. $2\overline{)728} =$
4. $3\overline{)309} =$

b) **Divide by 2 using short division:**

1. £2.16 2. £6.46
3. £5.42 4. £7.98

a) **Practise using short division by answering these questions:**

1. $4\overline{)123} =$
2. $5\overline{)133} =$
3. $6\overline{)135} =$
4. $5\overline{)234} =$

b) **Divide by 3 using short division:**

1. £9.33 2. £4.26
3. £7.14 4. £10.80

a) **Practise using short division by answering these questions:**

1. $8\overline{)5678} =$
2. $6\overline{)2257} =$
3. $2\overline{)4.85} =$
4. $3\overline{)4.35} =$

b) **Divide using short division:**

1. $7\overline{)£7.14} =$
2. $6\overline{)£7.38} =$
3. $9\overline{)£3.24} =$
4. $8\overline{)£8.96} =$

- **If there is a remainder, you can just write r.**

Checking results of calculations

It is important that we check our answers to make sure they make sense and that we have not made a mistake.

- Check with the inverse operation when using a calculator. For example, if you have worked out $345 \times 32 = 11040$, check this is correct by typing in $11040 \div 32$.
- Check the sum of several numbers by adding in a different order.
- Check with an equivalent sum. For example, if you have worked out $34 + 39 = 73$, check this is correct by working out $34 + 30 + 9$.

a) Check the following sums using your calculator. Mark them right or wrong.

1. $35 \times 76 = 2660$
2. $456 + 753 = 1208$
3. $987 - 379 = 609$

b) Add up these sums and then check by adding them in a different order:

1. $9 + 4 + 5 =$
2. $5 + 3 + 6 =$
3. $8 + 7 + 4 =$

c) Work out these sums and the equivalent calculation:

1. $24 + 25 =$
   $(24 \times 2) + 1 =$
2. $13 + 29 =$
   $(13 + 30) - 1 =$
3. $25 + 62 =$
   $25 + 60 + 2 =$

a) Using your calculator, copy and complete these sums:

1. $\square + 345 = 685$
2. $456 - \square = 103$
3. $45 \times \square = 585$

b) Add up these sums and then check by adding them in a different order:

1. $11 + 12 + 6 + 5 =$
2. $9 + 5 + 12 + 13 =$
3. $25 + 12 + 9 + 8 =$

c) Work out these sums and the equivalent calculation:

1. $125 + 126 =$
2. $654 + 199 =$
3. $563 - 21 =$

a) Using your calculator, copy and complete these sums:

1. $67.45 - \square = 12.09$
2. $678 \times \square = 155.94$
3. $8429 \div \square = 42145$

b) Add up these sums and then check by adding them in a different order:

1. $0.23 + 0.36 + 0.3 + 0.2 =$
2. $0.58 + 0.12 + 0.04 + 0.03 =$
3. $145 + 12 + 11 + 15 =$

c) Work out these sums and the equivalent calculation:

1. $5689 + 1999 =$
2. $5698 - 2566 =$
3. $12.36 - 6.98 =$

Checking results by approximating

Another way to check your answers is to approximate. That means to round the numbers in the sum to the nearest 10, 100 or 1000 so that you know roughly what the answer should look like.

a) Round these numbers to the nearest 10:

1. 62

2. 16

3. 92

b) Estimate the answer by rounding each number to its nearest 10 and then adding:

1. 19 + 21 =

2. 43 + 32 =

3. 51 + 42 =

c) Estimate the answer by rounding each number to its nearest 10 and then multiplying:

1. 28 × 39 =

2. 11 × 35 =

3. 31 × 27 =

a) Round these numbers to the nearest 100:

1. 282

2. 817

3. 307

b) Estimate the answer by rounding each number and then adding:

1. 108 + 21 =

2. 213 + 19 =

3. 168 + 19 =

c) Estimate the answer by rounding each number and then multiplying:

1. 382 × 18 =

2. 431 × 21 =

3. 410 × 23 =

a) Round these numbers to the nearest 1000:

1. 6282

2. 8175

3. 3507

b) Estimate the answer by rounding each number and then adding:

1. 1908 + 201 =

2. 2713 + 419 =

3. 4168 + 619 =

c) Estimate the answer by rounding each number and then multiplying:

1. 1382 × 18 =

2. 2431 × 21 =

3. 3410 × 23 =

Training Tips

- **Round digits less than 5 down.**
- **Round digits 5 or more up.**

Length

We use the following measurements to measure **length**.

mm = millimetres	1 km = 1000 m
cm = centimetres	1 m = 100 cm
m = metres	1 m = 1000 mm
km = kilometres	1 cm = 10 mm

Use these facts to help you answer the questions.

a) Convert these measurements:

1. 6 m = □ cm
2. 9 m = □ cm
3. 7 m = □ mm

b) Suggest suitable units for these:

1. Length of an ant
2. Distance from London to Scotland
3. Length of a paper clip

c) Measure these lines in cm:

1. ____________________
2. __________________________________
3. ______

a) Convert these measurements:

1. 17 m = □ cm
2. 64 m = □ mm
3. 120 km = □ m

b) Suggest suitable units for these:

1. Width of your book
2. Length of school hall
3. Length of a fly

c) Measure these lines in mm:

1. _____
2. _______________
3. __________

Gold

a) Convert these measurements:

1. 1500 mm = □ cm
2. 25000 m = □ km
3. 48000 cm = □ m

b) Suggest suitable units for these:

1. Distance from England to Africa
2. Length of a CD box
3. Length of a pin

c) Measure these lines in mm:

1. _____________________
2. __________________
3. ________________________________

- **Remember:**
  × 10 digits move one place to the left.

Mass

When we weigh objects we find their **mass**.

1 kilogram (kg) = 1000 grams (g)

6 kg = (6 × 1000) = 6000 g

a) Copy and complete:

1. 4 kg = □ g
2. 23 kg = □ g
3. 52 kg = □ g
4. 163 kg = □ g
5. 5000 g = □ kg

b) Suggest suitable units for the mass of:

1. An egg
2. A person
3. An elephant
4. A paper clip
5. A boot

a) Convert the following to grams and kilograms:

1. 8 kg = □ g
2. 8.941 kg = □ g
3. 6730 g = □ kg
4. 9800 g = □ kg

b) Suggest suitable units for the mass of:

1. A carrot
2. A car
3. A man
4. A slipper
5. A torch

a) Convert the following to grams and kilograms:

1. 0.086 kg = □ g
2. 6.28 kg = □ g
3. 1682 g = □ kg
4. 872 g = □ kg

b) Suggest suitable units for the mass of:

1. A CD case
2. A motorbike
3. A boat
4. A model aeroplane
5. A caravan

- **× 1000 digit moves 3 places to the left and ÷ 1000 digit moves 3 places to the right.**

Capacity

Measures of **capacity** are normally used for liquids.

1 litre (l) = 1000 millilitres (ml)

a) Convert to ml and litres:

1. 6 l
2. 12 l
3. 8 l
4. 8000 ml
5. 12000 ml
6. 4000 ml

b) Suggest suitable units to measure the following capacities:

1. A fish tank
2. A cup of water
3. A lake
4. A kettle
5. A spoonful of medicine

a) Convert to ml and litres:

1. 36 l
2. 6.30 l
3. 27.40 l
4. 7000 ml
5. 620 ml
6. 8940 ml

b) Suggest suitable units to measure the following capacities:

1. A swimming pool
2. A bowl of water
3. A petrol tank in a car
4. A bottle of perfume
5. An eggcup

a) Convert to ml and litres:

1. 0.043 l
2. 0.621 l
3. 0.4 l
4. 1498 ml
5. 270 ml
6. 46 ml

b) Suggest suitable units to measure the following capacities:

1. A bath
2. A pond
3. A jug of water
4. A teaspoon
5. A sink

- **× 1000 each digit moves 3 places to the left and ÷ 1000 each digit moves 3 places to the right.**

Area

Area is the size of a surface or the amount of space it covers.

Using squares can help work out the area of shapes.
The area of this shape is 8 squares.

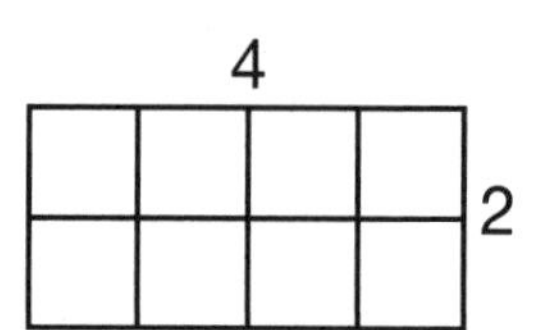

For a rectangle, you can also use this rule: **Area = Length × Breadth**

a) Work out the areas of these shapes by counting squares:

1. 5, 2

2. 3, 2, 4

b) Work out the areas of the following using the rule:

1. 4, 2

2. 5, 3

c) Draw a shape with an area of:

1. 12 squares

2. 24 squares

a) Work out the areas of the following using the rule:

1.

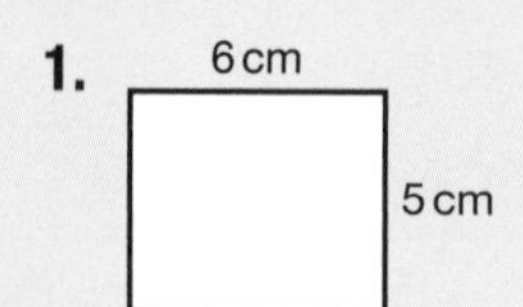

2.

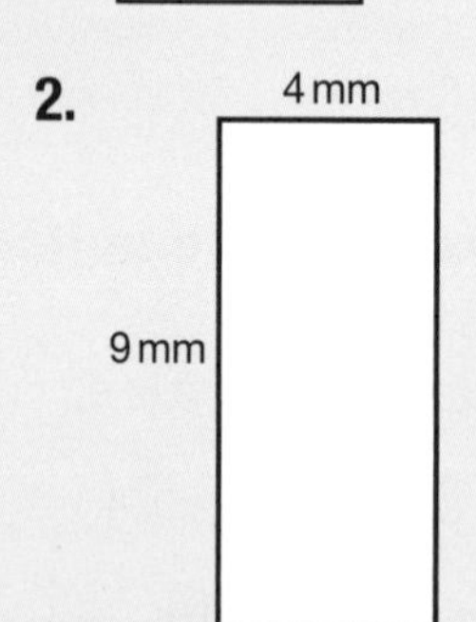

b) Measure these rectangles in mm and work out their area:

1.

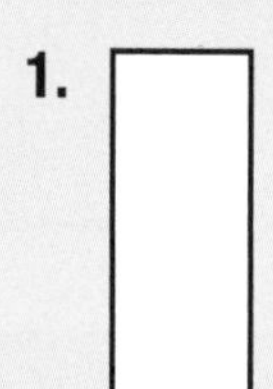

2.

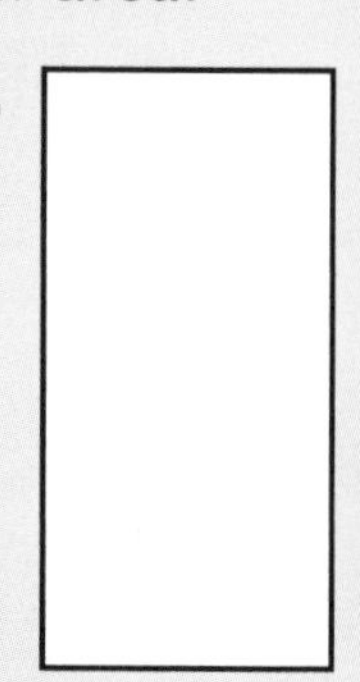

c) Draw a shape on cm² paper with an area of:

1. 26 cm² **2.** 19 cm²

a) Work out the areas of these shapes:

1. 11, 9, 3, 2

2.

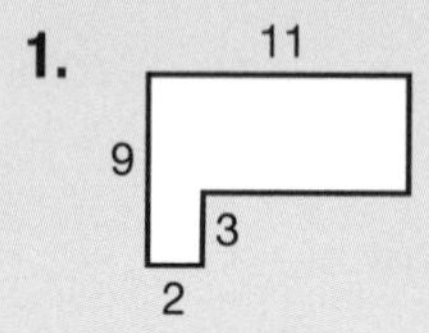

b) Measure these rectangles, to the nearest mm, and find the area:

1.

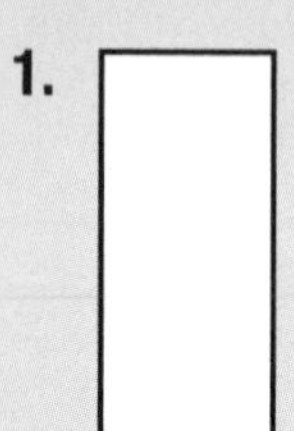

2.

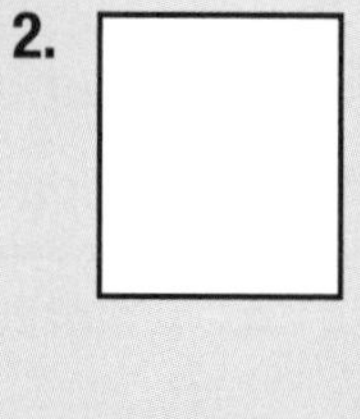

c) Draw a shape on cm² paper with an area of:

1. 270 mm² **2.** 64 mm²

- **Remember to check units: mm², cm², km².**

Perimeter

Perimeter is the distance around the outside of a closed shape.

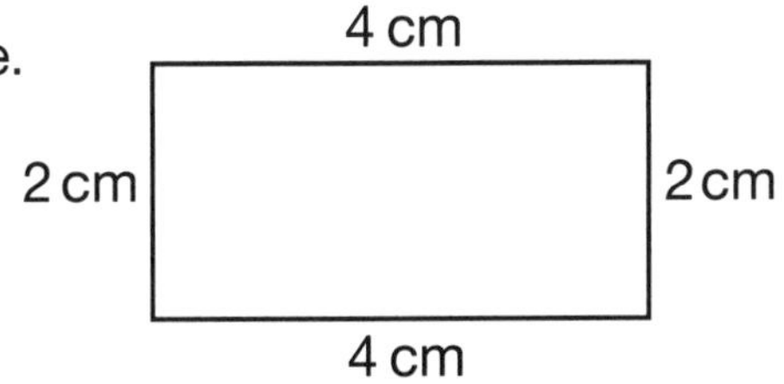

Example

Perimeter = 4 cm + 2 cm + 4 cm + 2 cm
= 12 cm

a) Work out the perimeters of these shapes:

1.

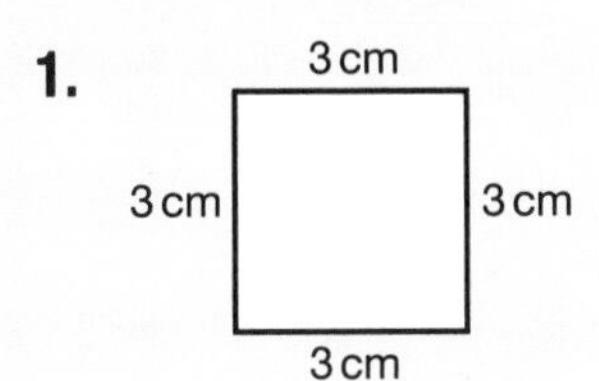

2.

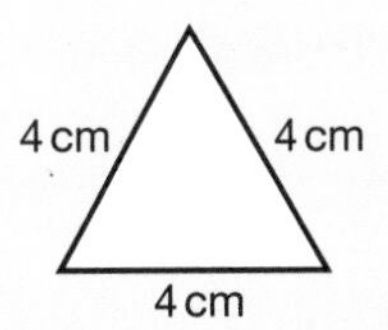

b) Measure the sides of these shapes in cm and find the perimeter:

1.

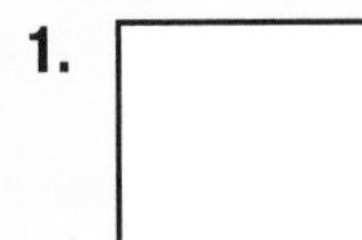

2.

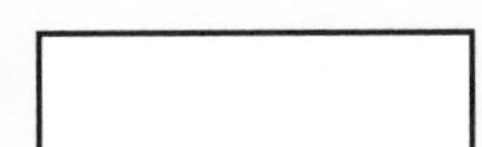

c) Draw a shape with perimeter of:

1. 8 cm

2. 12 cm

3. 24 cm

a) Work out the perimeters of these shapes:

1.

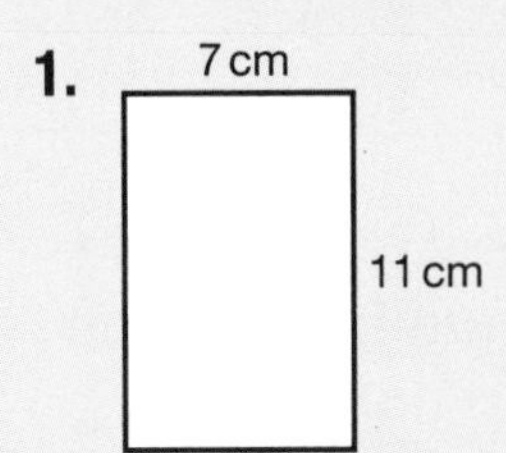

2.

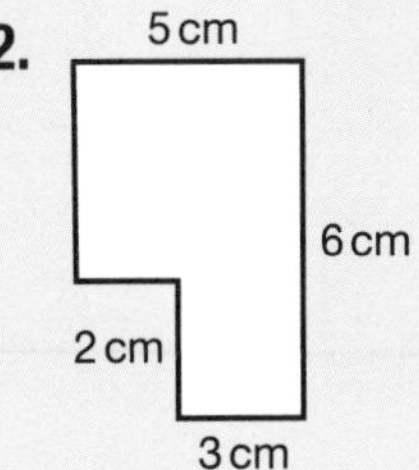

b) Measure the perimeters of these shapes to the nearest cm:

1.

2.

c) Draw an irregular shape with perimeter:

1. 36 cm **2.** 22.5 cm

3. 19 cm

a) Find the perimeter of:

1. A regular octagon with sides 7 cm

2. A square with sides 12 mm

3. A regular decagon with sides 13 cm

b) Measure the perimeters of the following shapes in mm:

1.

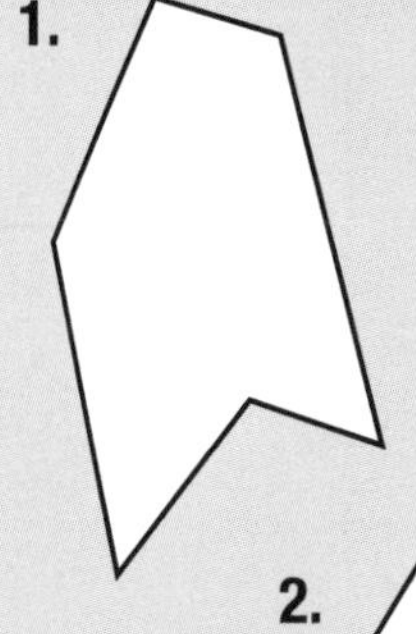

2.

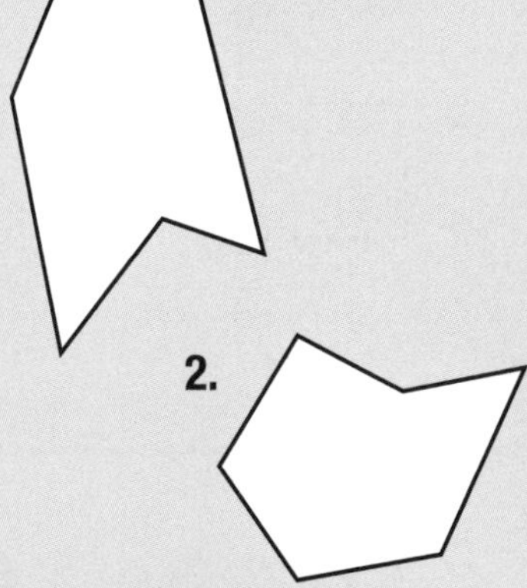

c) Draw a shape with perimeter:

1. 36 cm **2.** 142 mm

3. 72 cm

Reading from scales

Before trying to read any scales, work out what the scale is telling you.
What are the first and last numbers?

Bronze

a) Work out what number each letter is pointing to.

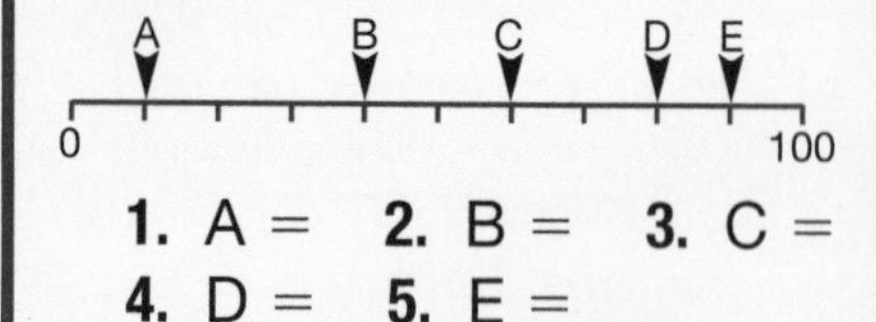

1. A = **2.** B = **3.** C =
4. D = **5.** E =

b) On the vertical scale what number is each letter pointing to?

1. F = **2.** G = **3.** H =
4. I = **5.** J =

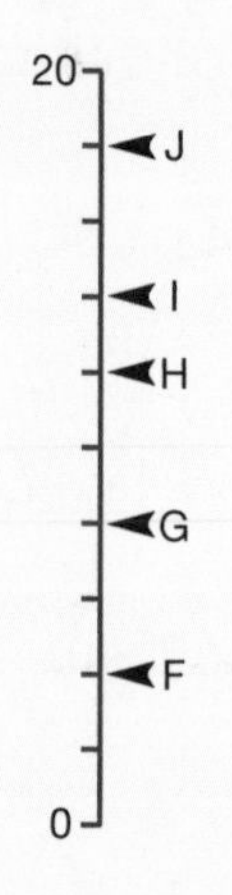

Silver

a) Work out what number each letter is pointing to.

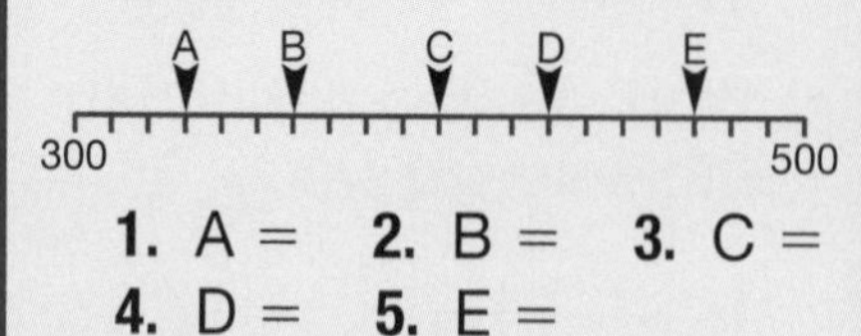

1. A = **2.** B = **3.** C =
4. D = **5.** E =

b) On the vertical scale what number is each letter pointing to?

1. F = **2.** G = **3.** H =
4. I = **5.** J =

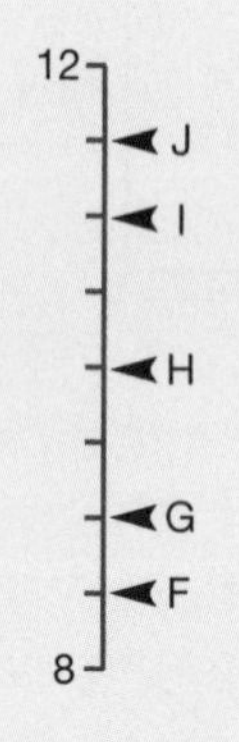

Gold

a) On the vertical scale what number is each letter pointing to?

1. F = **2.** G = **3.** H =
4. I = **5.** J =

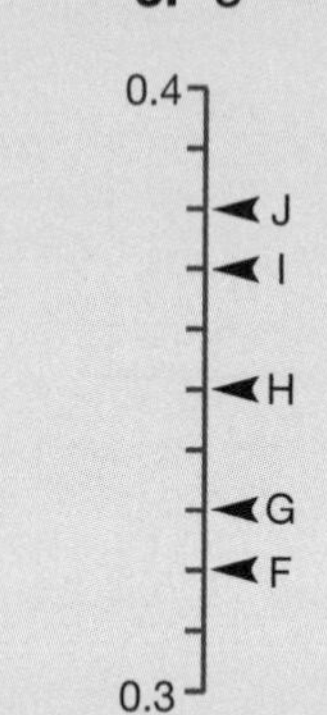

b) What number is each letter pointing to?

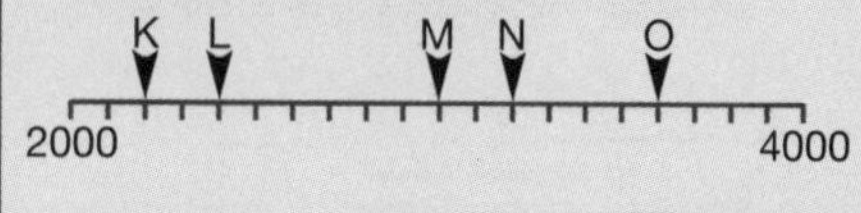

1. K = **2.** L = **3.** M =
4. N = **5.** O =

- Work out the scale before you start.

Time

We measure time in a lot of ways:
1 minute = 60 seconds, 1 hour = 60 minutes, 1 day = 24 hours,
1 week = 7 days, 1 year = 365 days

Analogue

Digital

When we read the time we can read analogue and digital clocks.

Digital clocks use the 24-hour system.
Any time after 12:00 on a digital clock shows it is a time after midday.

Analogue clocks use a.m. and p.m. to show if it is the morning or afternoon.

Use this table to answer the questions:

	Starts	Finishes
Blue Peter	5 p.m.	5.30 p.m.
News	5.30 p.m.	6.10 p.m.
Transformers	6.10 p.m.	6.30 p.m.

1. For how many minutes is Blue Peter on?
2. For how many minutes is Transformers on?
3. If I watch the News and Transformers, how long will I be watching TV?

Use this table to answer the questions:

BUS TIMETABLE				
School	12:30	13:01	13:32	14:03
Hospital	12:35	13:06	13:37	14:08
Shops	12:42	13:13	13:44	14:15
Station	12:53	13:24	13:55	14:26

1. How long does the journey take from the School to the Shops?
2. How long does the journey take from the Hospital to the Station?
3. If the bus leaves the Hospital at 14:08, what time will it reach the Station?

Use this train timetable to answer the questions:

London Victoria	07:42	——	09:25	11:24
Streatham Hill	09:02	10:09	10:45	12:44
West Norwood	09:12	——	10:55	12:54
Crystal Palace	09:22	——	11:05	13:04
West Croydon	09:37	10:44	11:20	13:19

1. How long does the journey take from London Victoria to West Norwood?
2. If I need to be in West Croydon for 11:00, what time train should I catch from West Norwood?
3. If I arrive at Crystal Palace at 1.04 p.m., what time train did I catch from Streatham Hill?

2D shapes

2D shapes have corners and sides. They are flat shapes.

These are some 2D shapes:

There are four different types of triangle:

Right-angled triangle
– It has a right angle (90°)

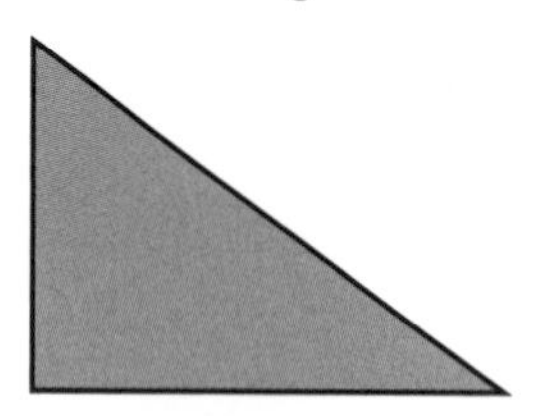

Equilateral triangle
– Has 3 sides that are equal
– Has 3 angles that are equal

Isosceles triangle
– 2 sides are equal length
– 2 equal angles

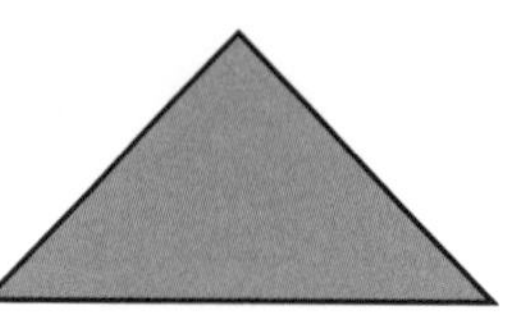

Scalene triangle
– No sides are equal
– No equal angles

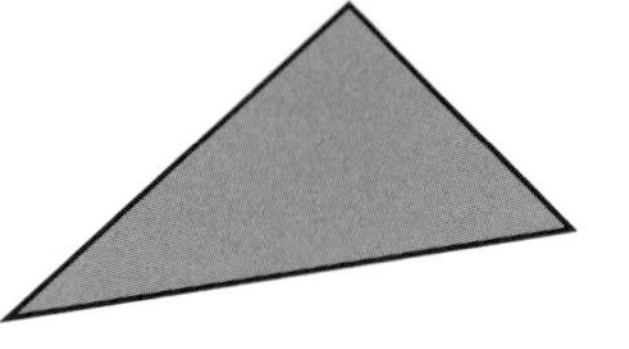

Bronze

a) Decide which type of triangles these are:

1. 

2. 

3. 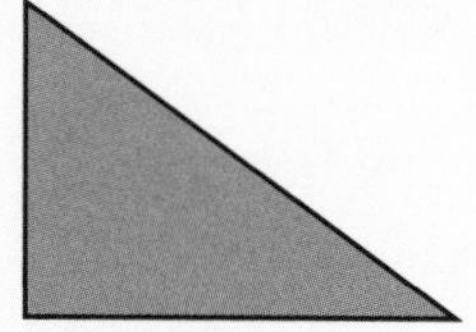

4. 

b) Name the following shapes:

1. 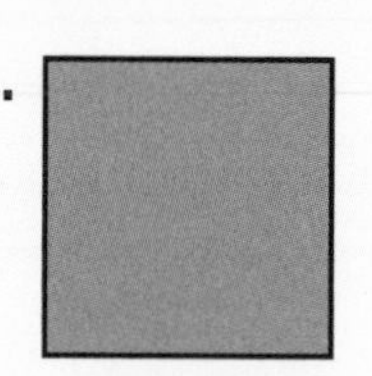

2. 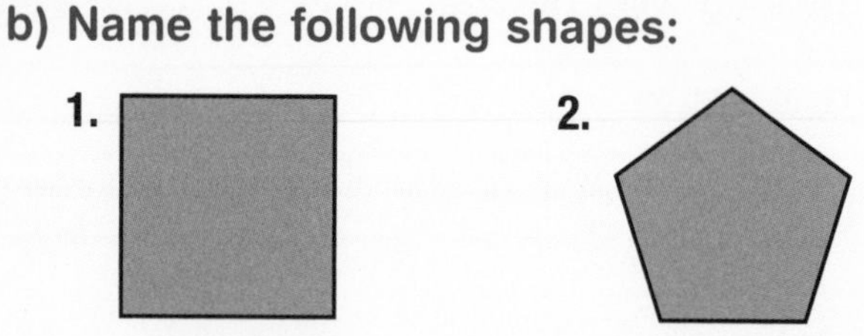

3. 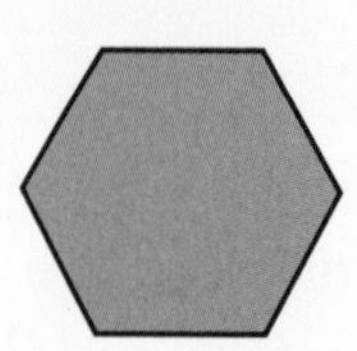

4. 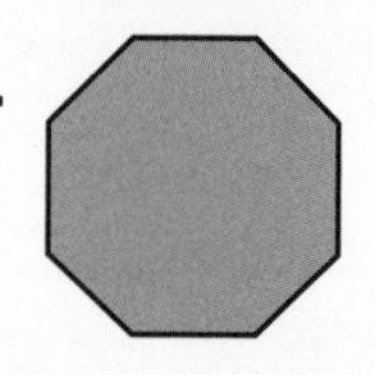

c) Write a description of each of the shapes above.

a) Name each triangle:

1. 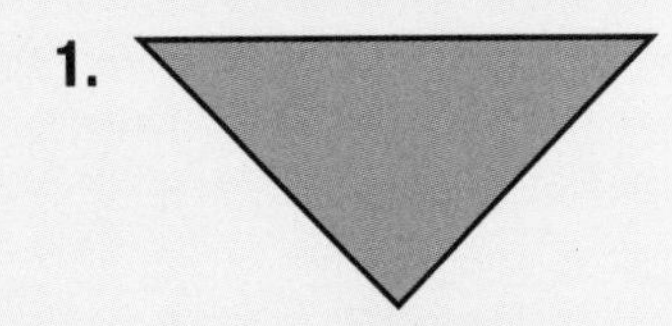

2. 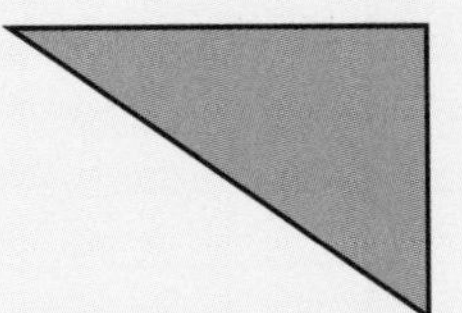

3.

4.

b) Name the following shapes:

1. 

2. 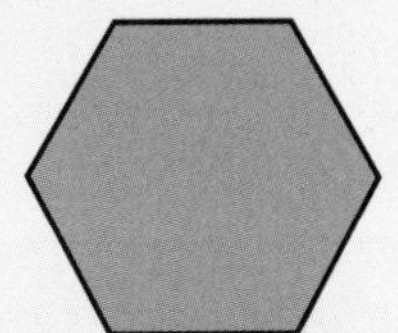

3. 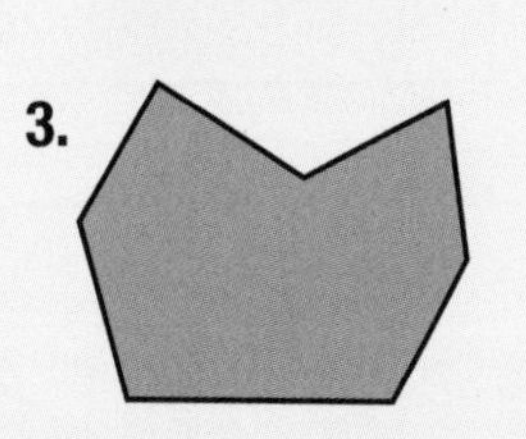

4. 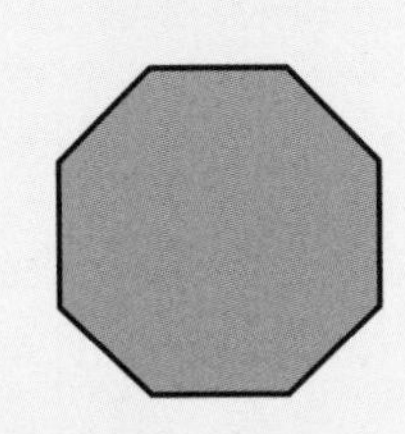

c) For each shape above, describe the shape's properties.

a) Draw the following shapes:

1. A right-angled scalene triangle
2. An equilateral triangle
3. A non right-angled isosceles triangle
4. A right-angled isosceles triangle

b) Draw the following shapes:

1. Trapezium
2. Parallelogram
3. Rhombus
4. Decagon

c) Name these shapes:

1. This shape has four right angles and all its sides are equal
2. This shape has only one pair of parallel sides
3. This shape has two pairs of parallel sides and no right angles

- **Use a ruler when drawing shapes.**

3D shapes

3D shapes have faces, edges and vertices.

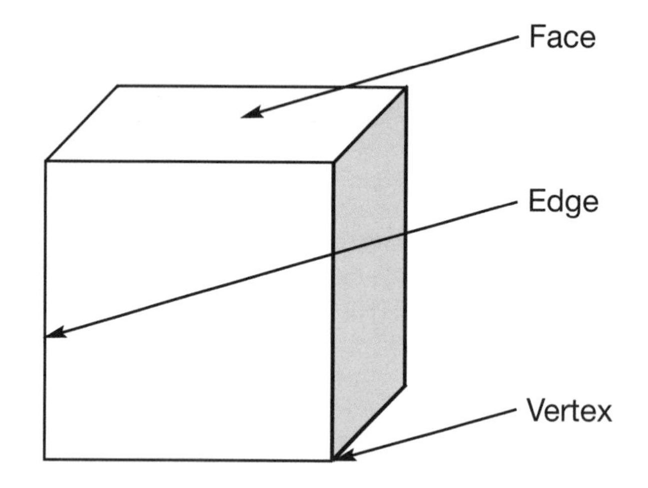

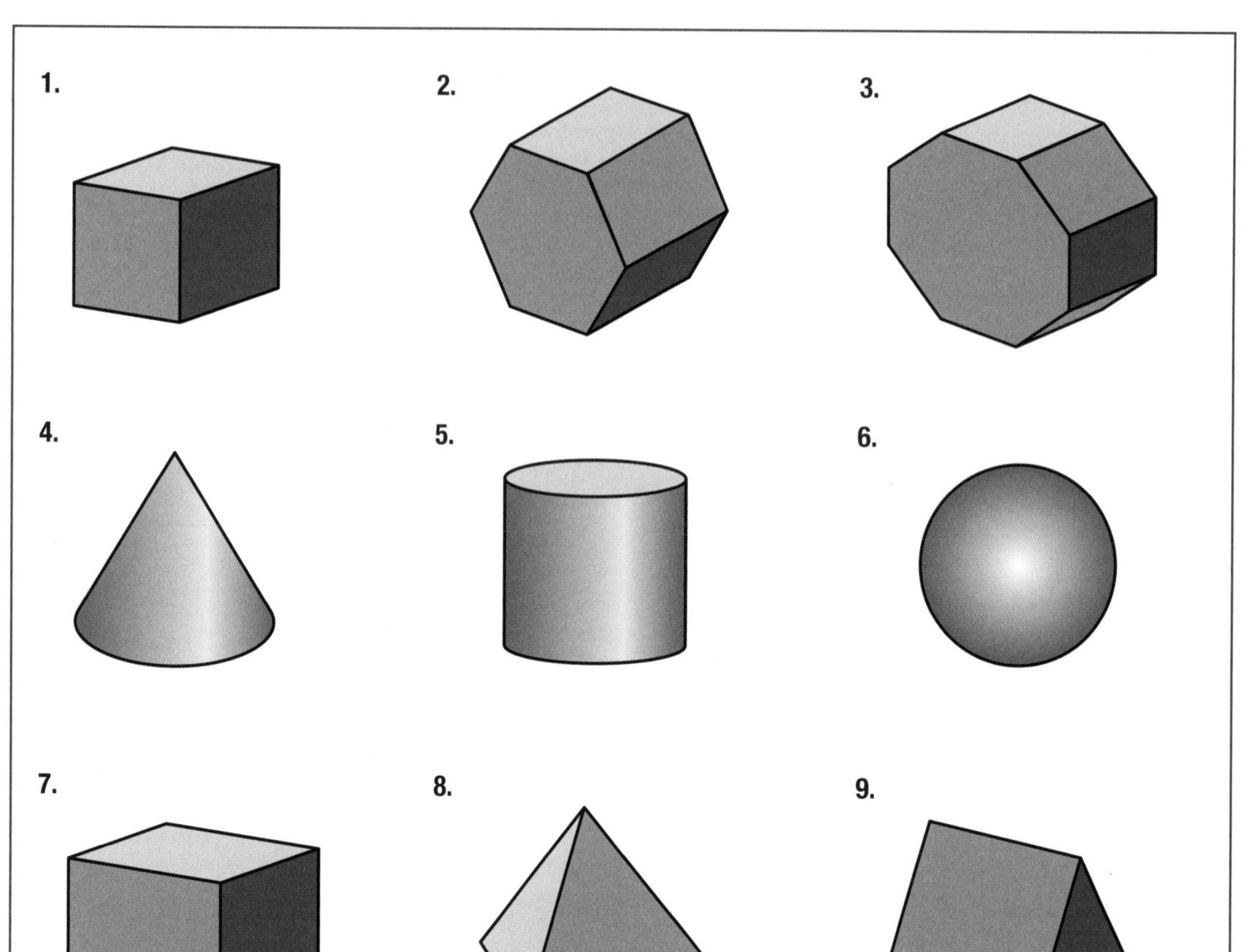

Name all 15 shapes.

Name each shape and say how many vertices, edges and faces each has.

For each shape, give:

- its name
- the shapes of all the faces
- the number of vertices, edges and faces

10.

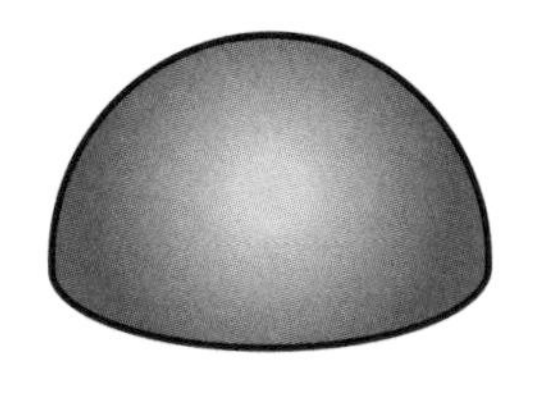

11.

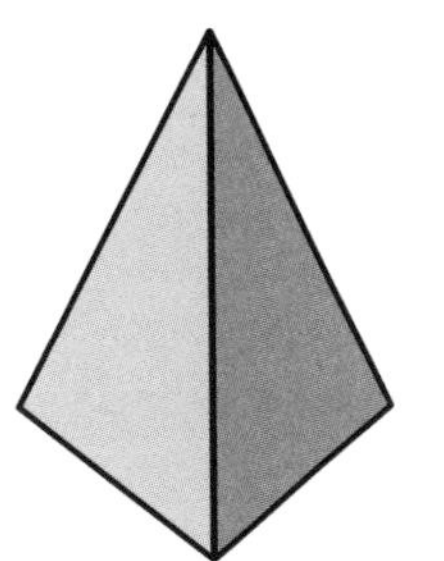

12.

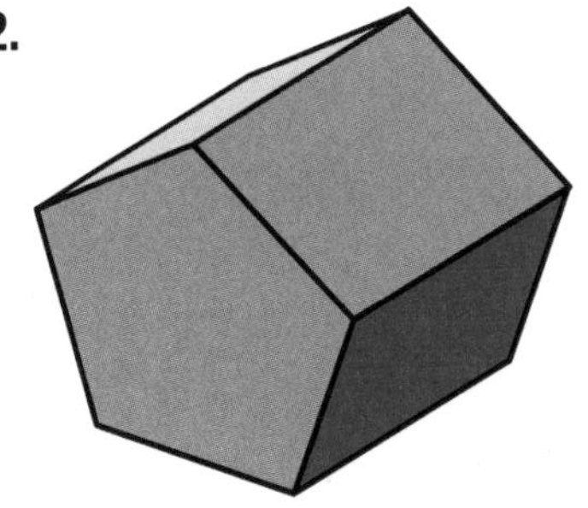

13.

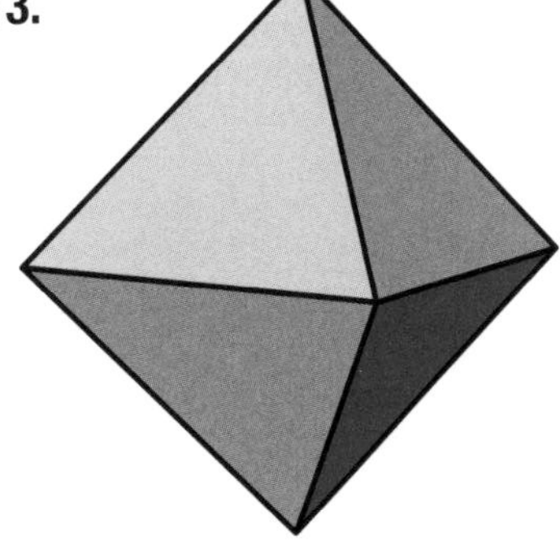

14.

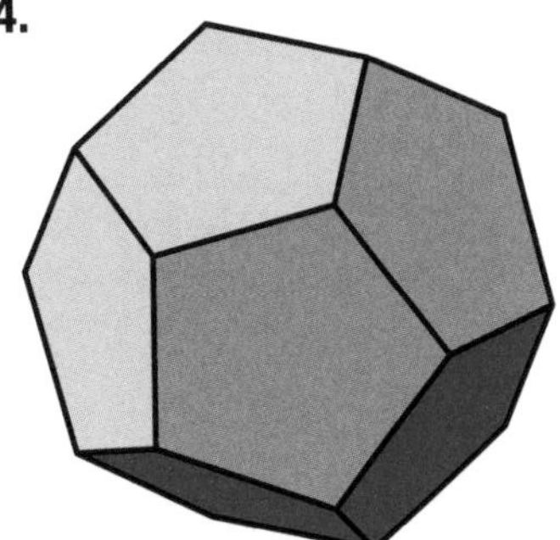

15.

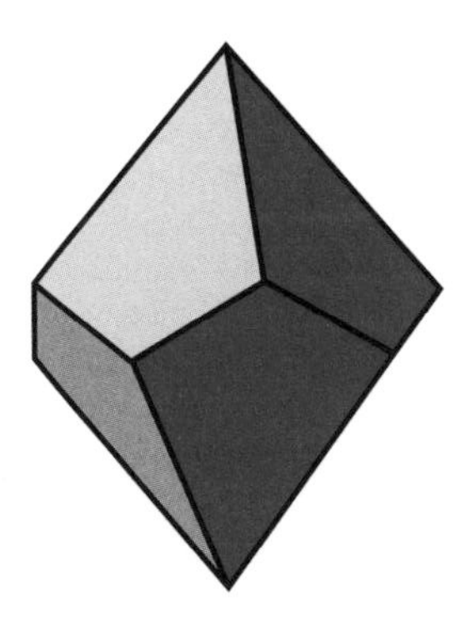

- 3D = three-dimensional

Visualise 3D shapes

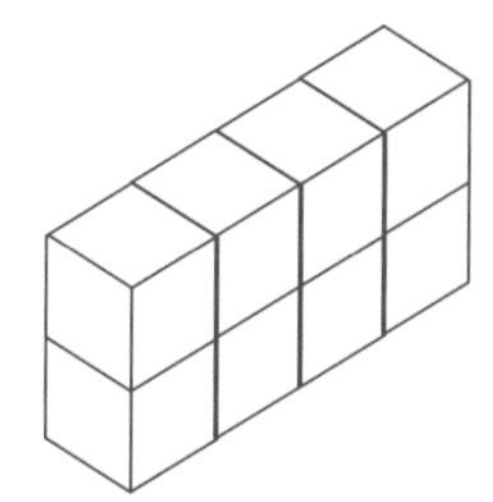

Look at this drawing of a 3D shape.
How many cubes are needed to make it?

The answer is 8.

On this page you are going to practise visualising 3D shapes from drawings.

A

B

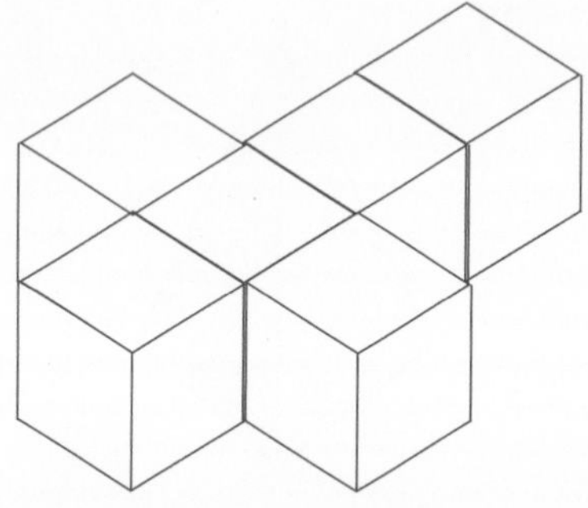

C

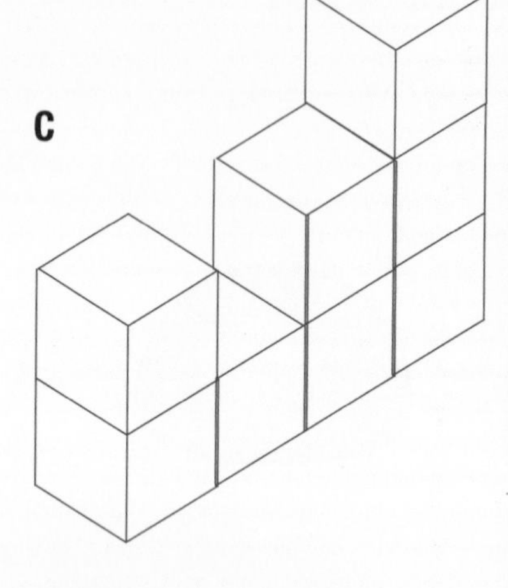

a) **How many cubes are there in these shapes?**

1. A =

2. B =

3. C =

b) **What is the least number of unit cubes needed to make the shapes into cuboids?**

1. A =

2. B =

3. C =

c) **What is the least number of unit cubes needed to make the shapes into cubes?**

1. A =

2. B =

3. C =

- **Try to visualise the cubes.**
- **Be careful not to count cubes twice.**

A

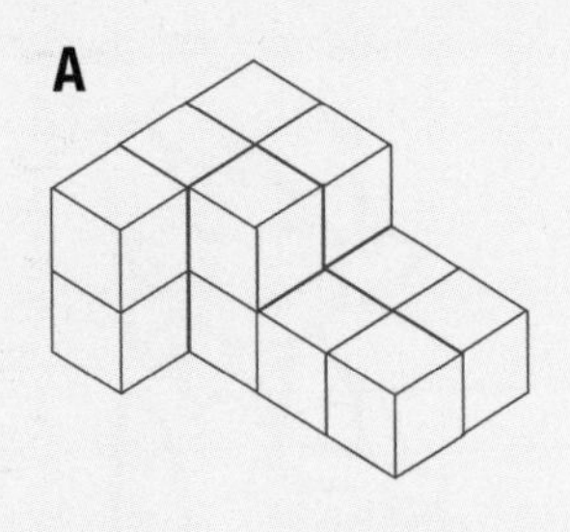

B

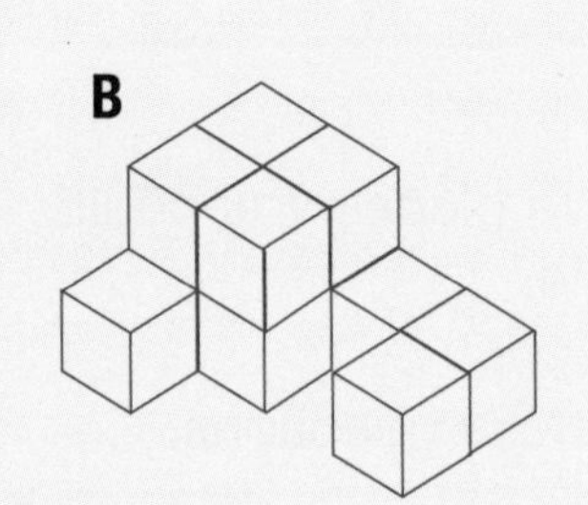

C

a) How many cubes are there in these shapes?

1. A = **2.** B = **3.** C =

b) What is the least number of unit cubes needed to make the shapes into cuboids?

1. A = **2.** B = **3.** C =

c) What is the least number of unit cubes needed to make the shapes into cubes?

1. A = **2.** B = **3.** C =

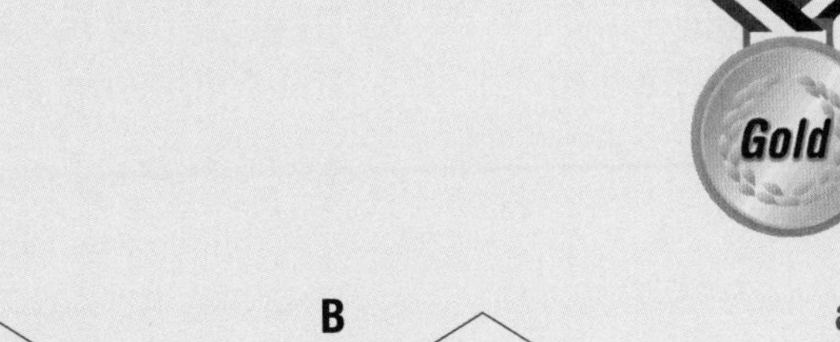

A

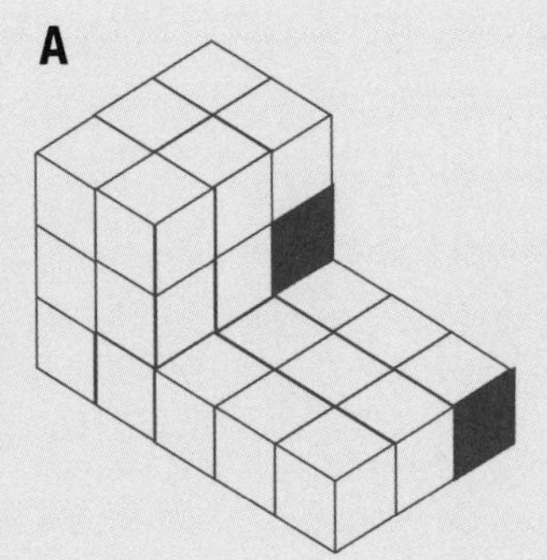

B

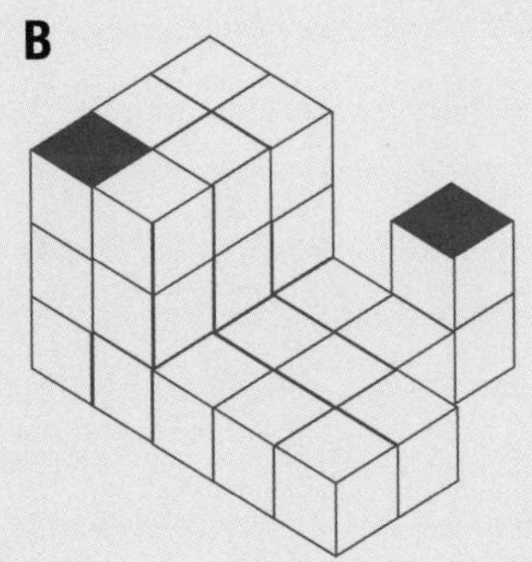

C

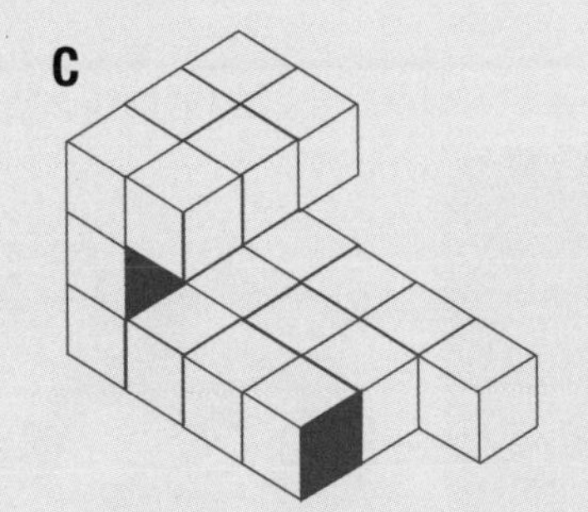

a) How many cubes are there in these shapes?

1. A = **2.** B = **3.** C =

b) How many cubes are needed to make the shapes into cuboids?

1. A = **2.** B = **3.** C =

c) What is the least number of unit cubes needed to cover and join the two shaded faces?

1. A = **2.** B = **3.** C =

Symmetry

Symmetry means a shape where two halves are a mirror image of each other.

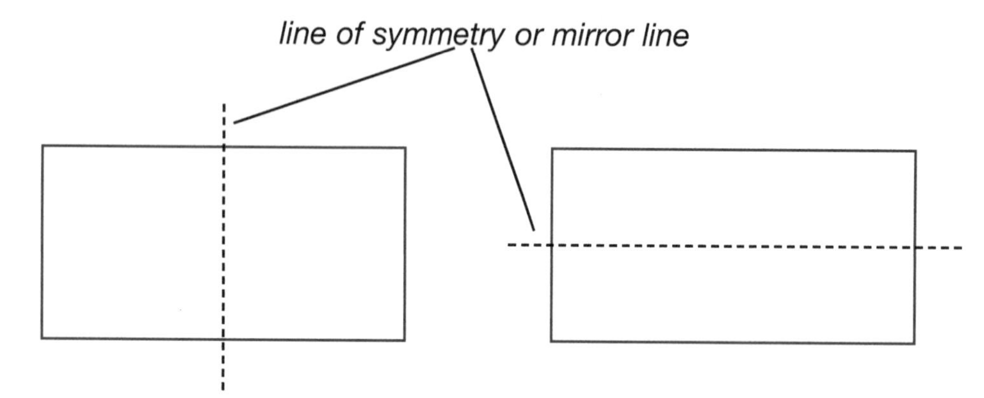

A rectangle has two lines of symmetry. There are two places you could place a mirror to get an exact image of the rectangle.

You may find that using a small mirror can help in these questions.

Bronze

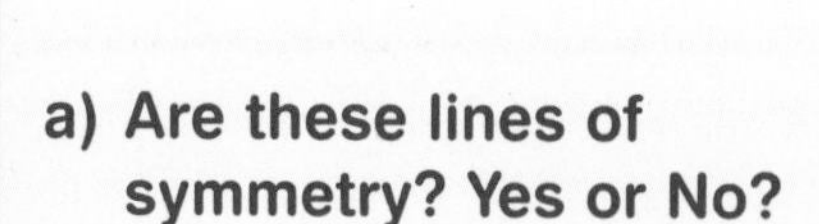

a) Are these lines of symmetry? Yes or No?

1.

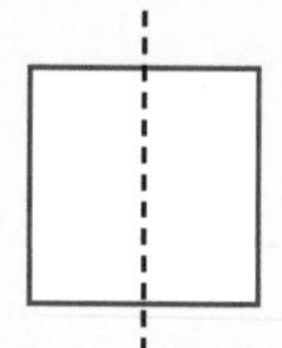

2.

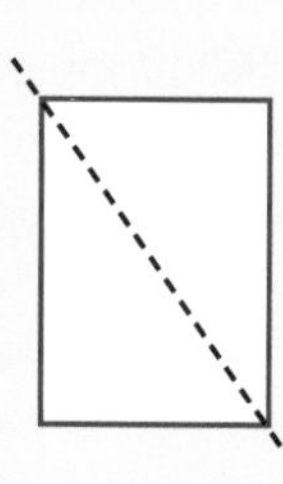

b) Complete these symmetrical patterns:

1.

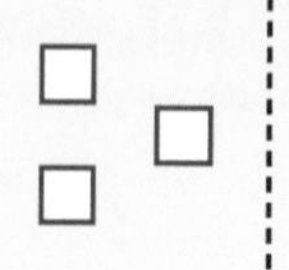

2.

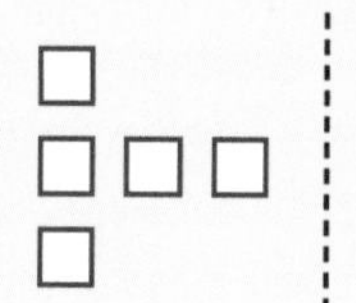

c) Sketch the reflection for the following shapes:

1.

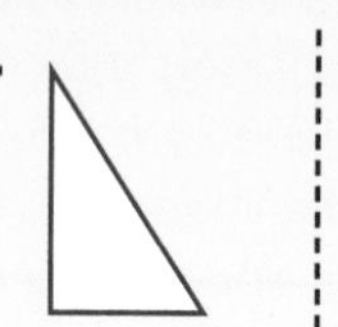

2.

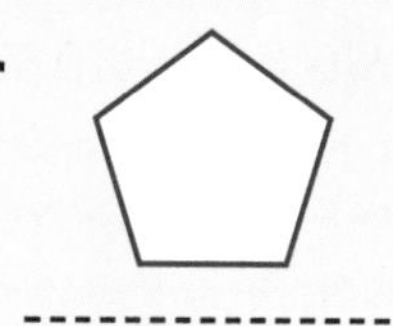

Training Tips

- **Check with a mirror.**
- **Spell: symmetry**
- **You can also check by cutting out a shape and folding it up.**

a) How many lines of symmetry are there in each shape?

1. 

2. 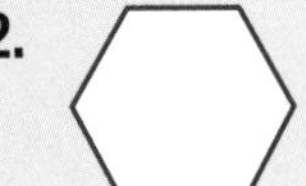

b) Complete these symmetrical patterns:

1. 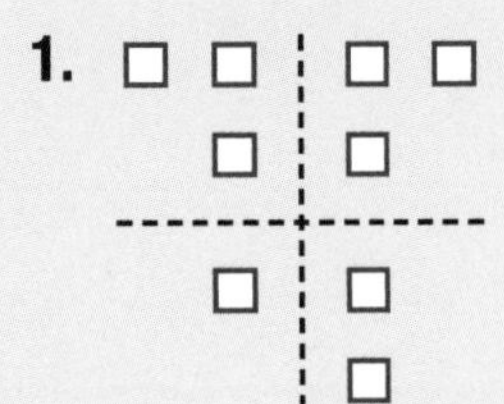

2.

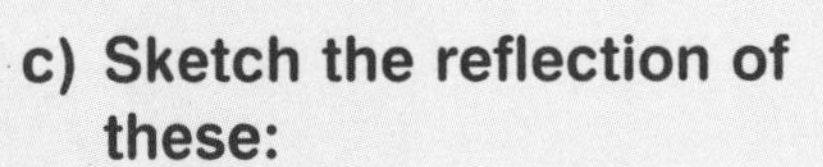

c) Sketch the reflection of these:

1. 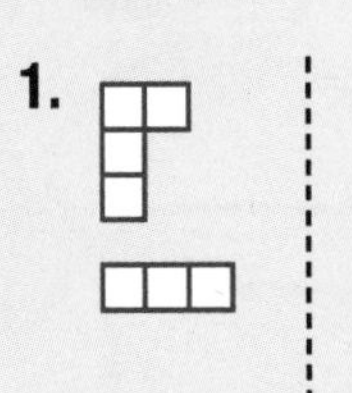

2.

a) Draw a shape with:

1. One line of symmetry
2. Two lines of symmetry
3. Four lines of symmetry
4. No lines of symmetry

b) Complete these symmetrical patterns in all four quadrants:

1. 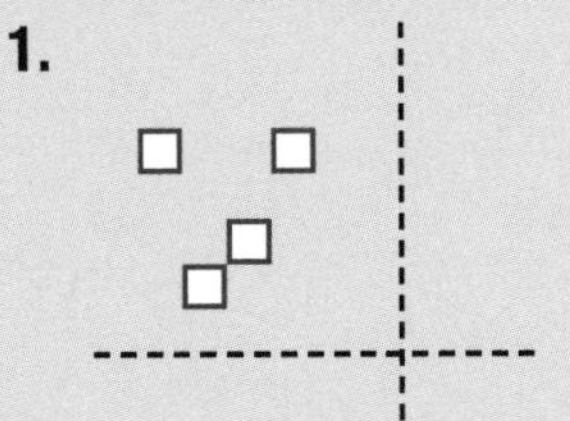

2.

c) Sketch reflections for the following:

1. 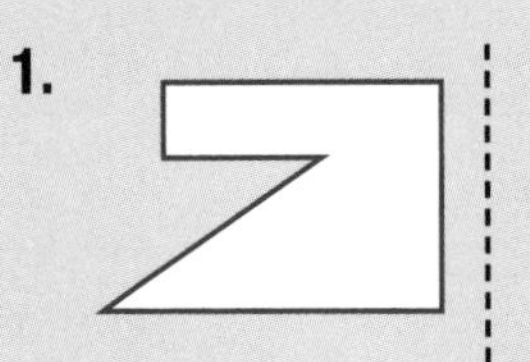

2. 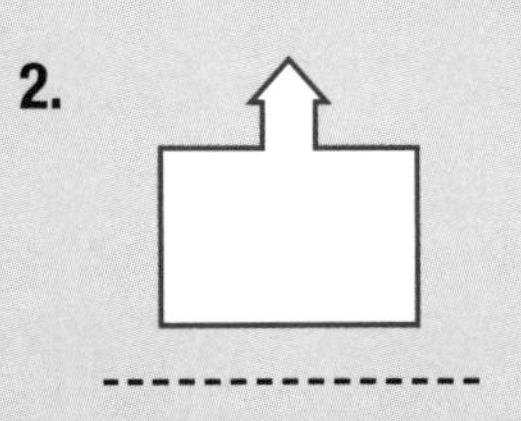

Nets

A net of a shape is a solid shape folded out flat.

Bronze

Can you make a cube out of these nets? Draw and cut them out to help.

1.

2.

3.

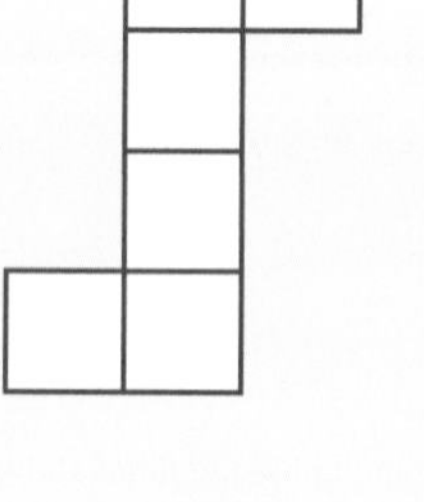

4.

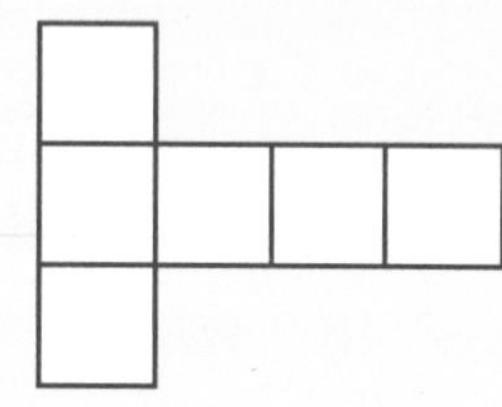

5.

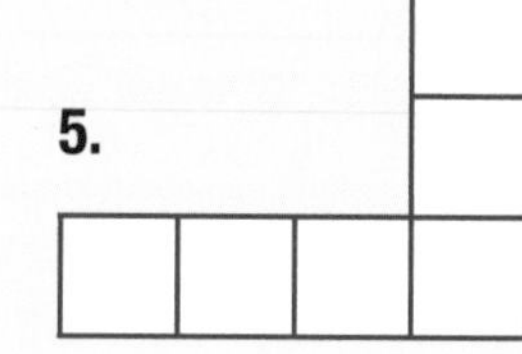

6.

7.

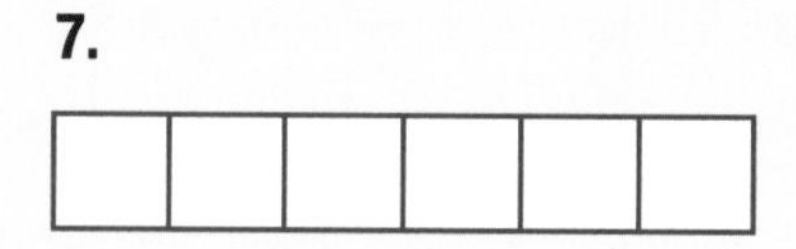

- Cutting out the nets and testing may help.
- Try to visualise folding the net.

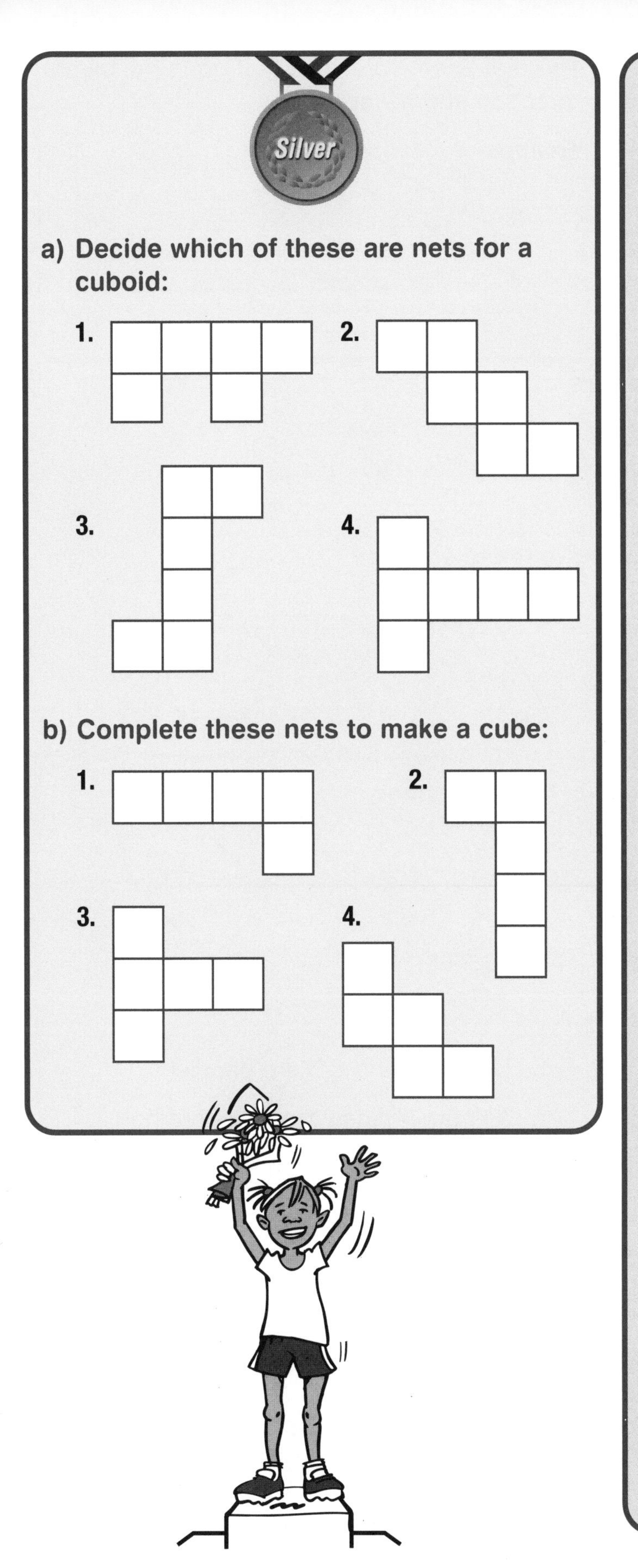

a) Decide which of these are nets for a cuboid:

1. 2.

3. 4.

b) Complete these nets to make a cube:

1. 2.

3. 4.

a) Can you make a cuboid from these nets?

1.

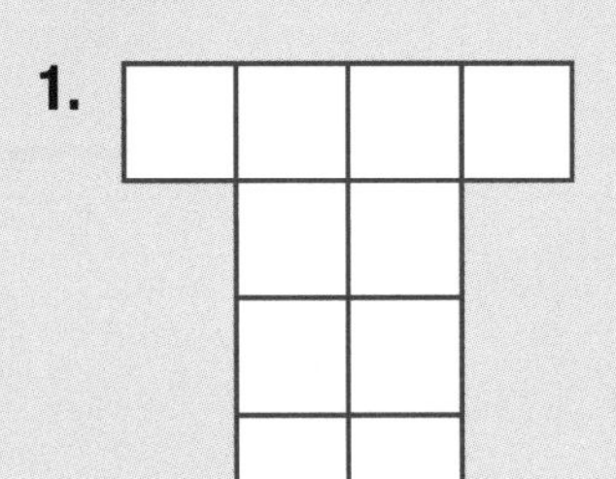

2.

3.

4.

b) Draw a net of:

1. A square-based pyramid
2. A triangular prism
3. A tetrahedron
4. A hexagonal prism

Perpendicular and parallel lines

Perpendicular lines – cross at right angles.

Example

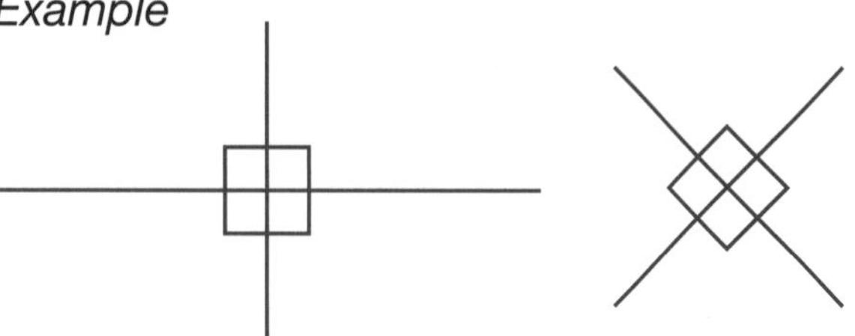

Parallel lines – are lines that go in the same direction and never cross.

Example

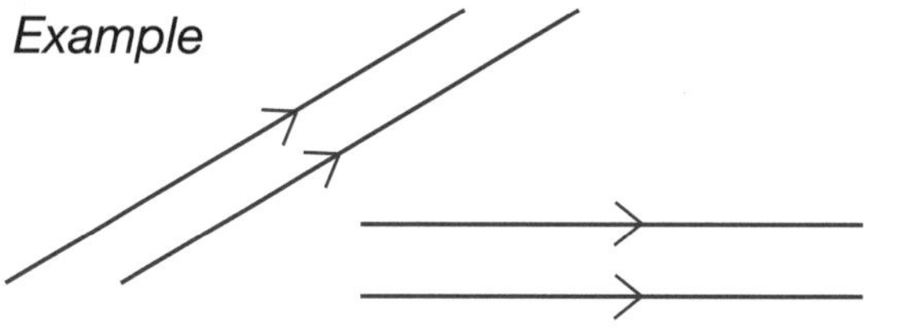

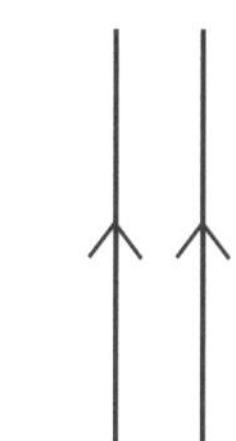

a) How many pairs of parallel lines can you see in these shapes?

1. 

2. 

3. 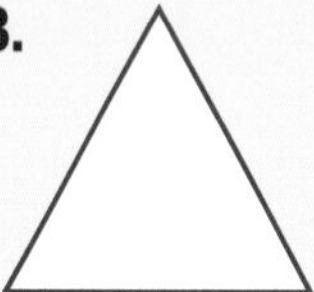

4. 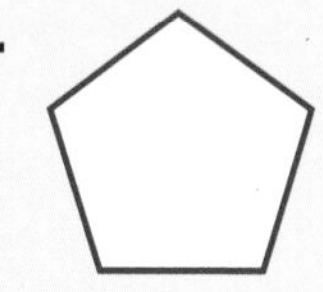

b) How many perpendicular lines can you see in these shapes?

1. 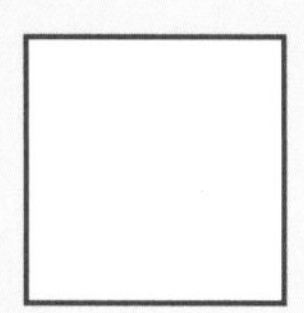

2. 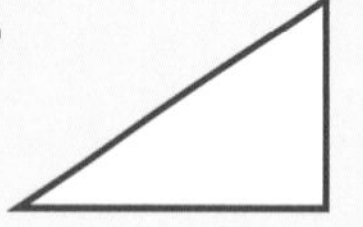

3. 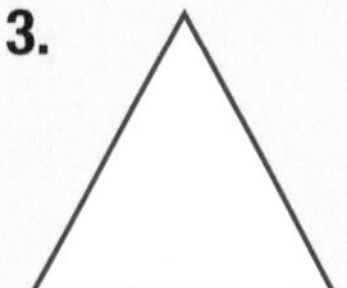

4. 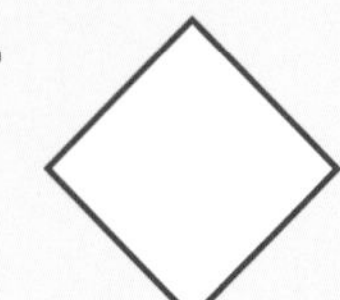

c) True or false?

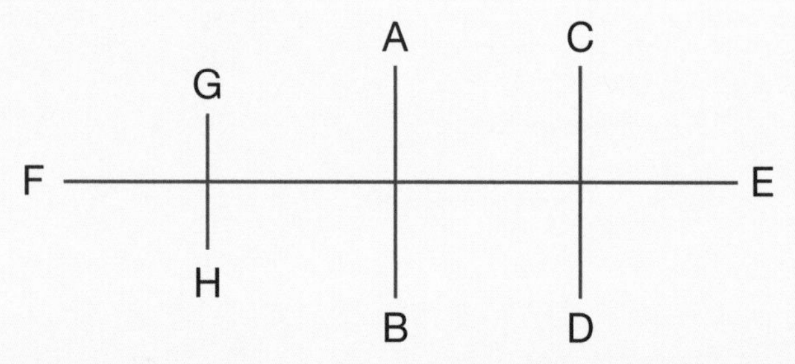

1. Lines AB and CD are parallel
2. All parallel lines cross each other
3. Lines GH and CD are parallel
4. Lines EF and CD are perpendicular

- **Make sure you can spell perpendicular and parallel.**
- **Look out for the different lines.**

a) How many pairs of parallel lines can you see in these diagrams?

1.

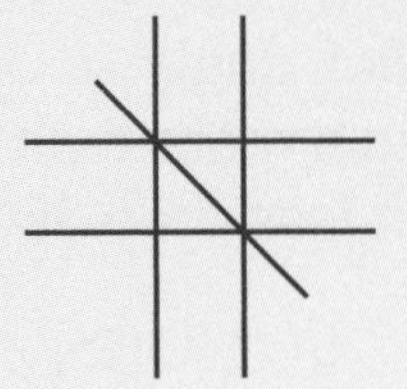

2.

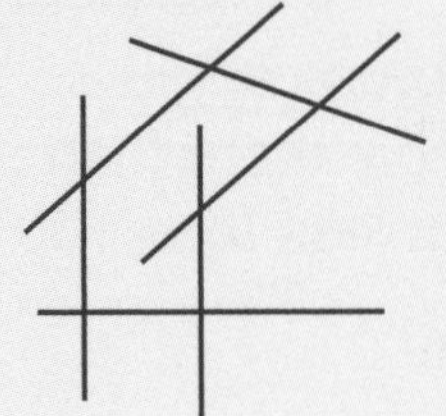

3.

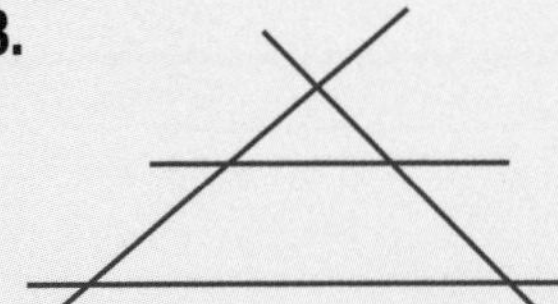

4.

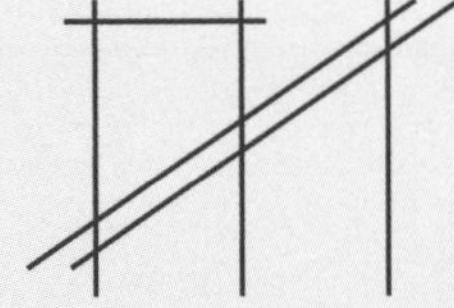

b) How many pairs of perpendicular lines can you see in the diagrams above?

c) True or false?

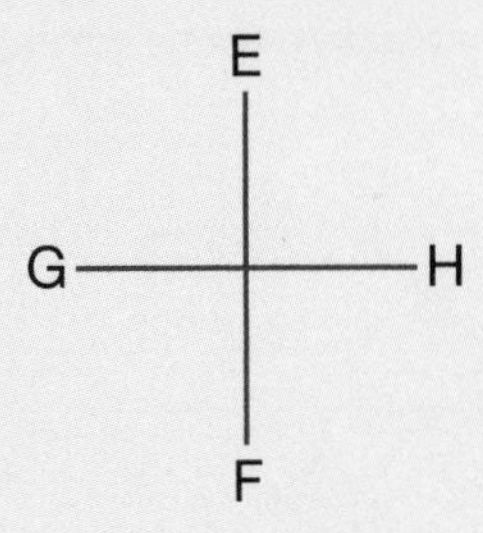

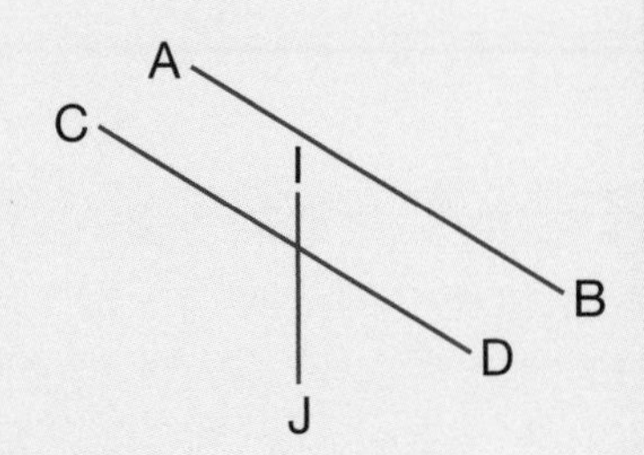

1. GH and IJ are parallel
2. EF and IJ are parallel
3. EF and GH are perpendicular
4. Perpendicular lines always cross each other

a) Draw the following shapes:

1. A shape with only 3 pairs of parallel lines
2. A shape with 4 pairs of perpendicular lines
3. A shape with 4 pairs of parallel lines
4. A shape with no parallel or perpendicular lines

b) Look at these shapes and describe how many parallel lines there are:

1.

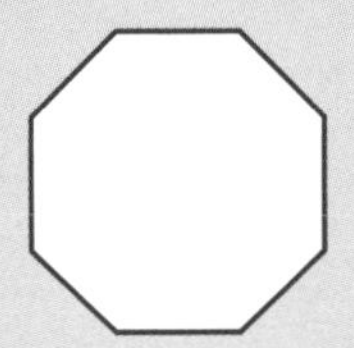

2.

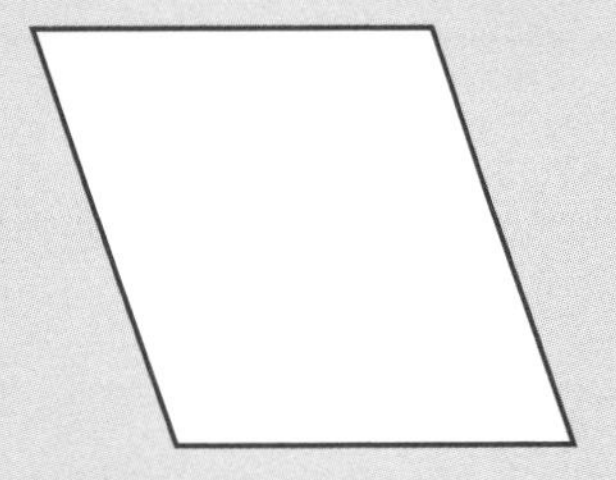

3.

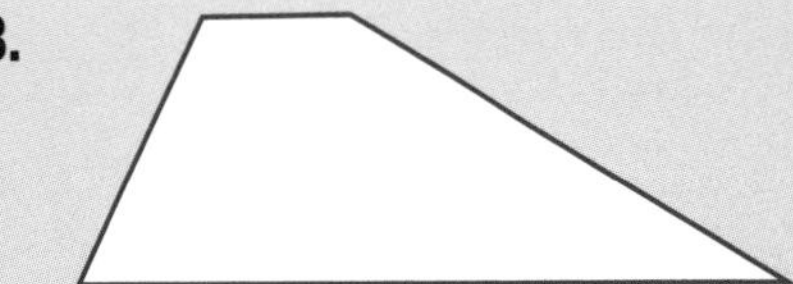

4.

Angles

An angle is a measure of space between two straight lines.

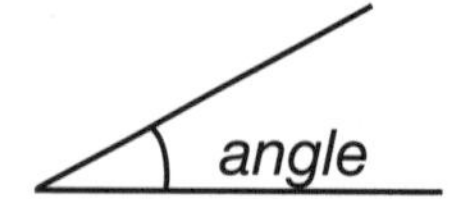

There are four different types of angle.

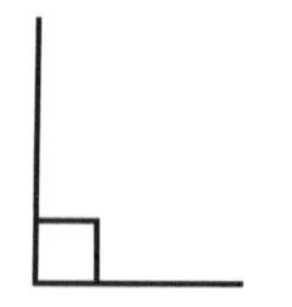

Right angle = 90°

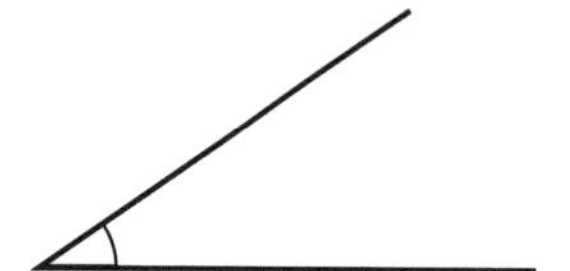

Acute angle = angle less than 90°

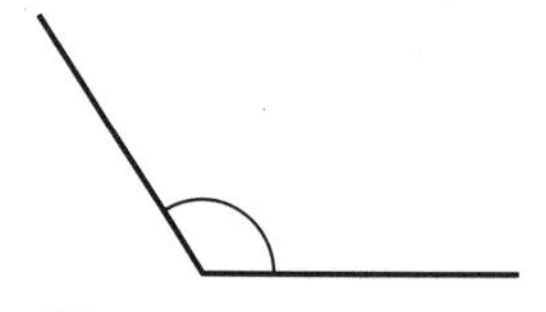

Obtuse angle = angle more than 90° but less than 180°

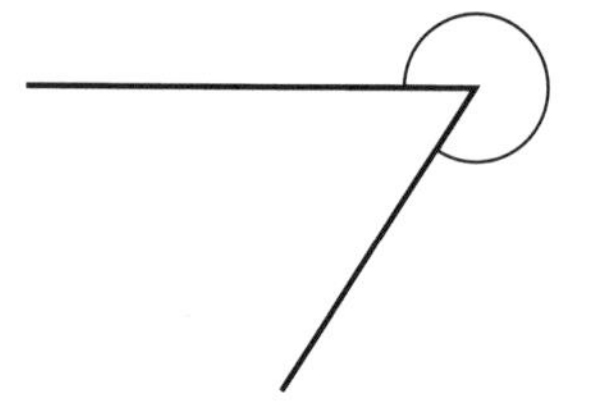

reflex angle = angle more than 180° but less than 360°

We measure angles in degrees (°) using a protractor.
You will need a protractor to answer these questions.

Bronze

a) Identify these angles as acute or obtuse:

1.

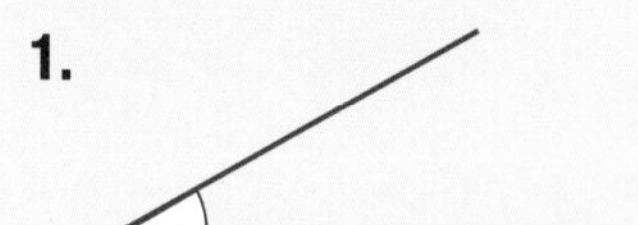

2.

3.

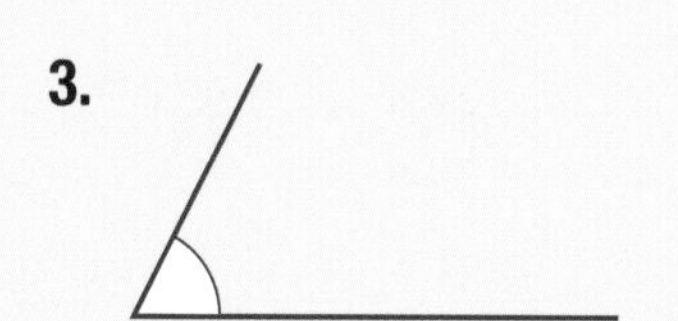

b) Estimate these angles:

1. 120° or 150°?

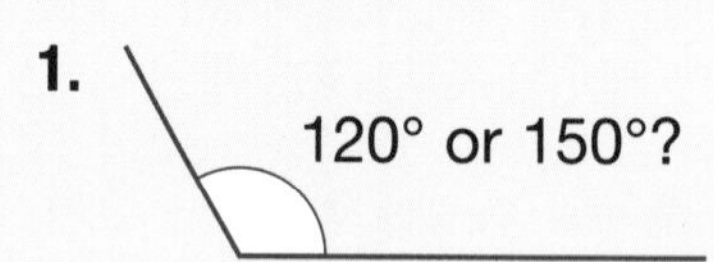

2. 30° or 60°?

3. 60° or 80°?

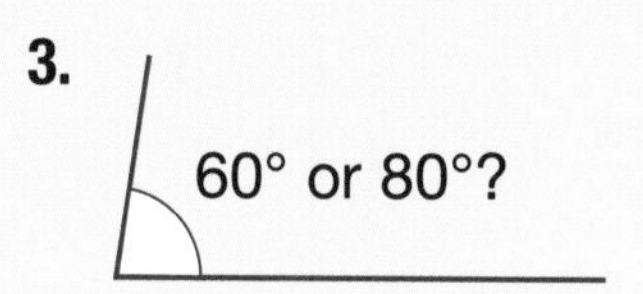

c) Measure these angles:

1.

2.

3.

- **Be careful which scale you use on a protractor.**

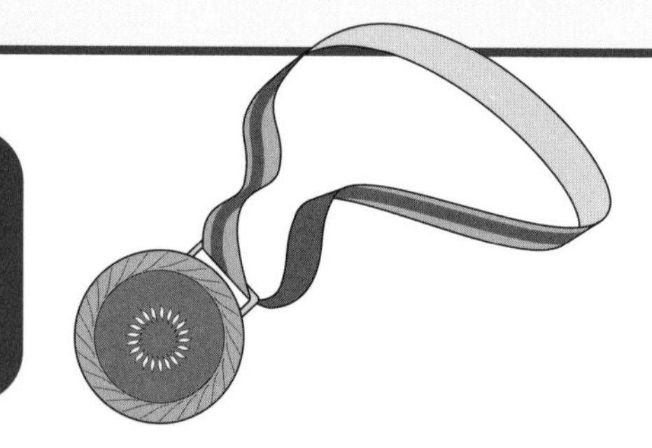

a) Identify these angles as acute or obtuse:

1.

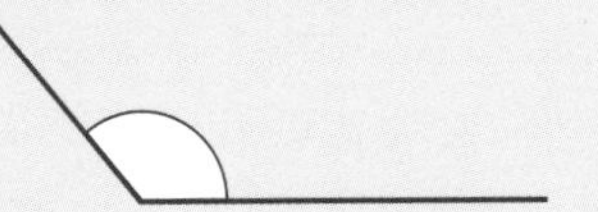

2.

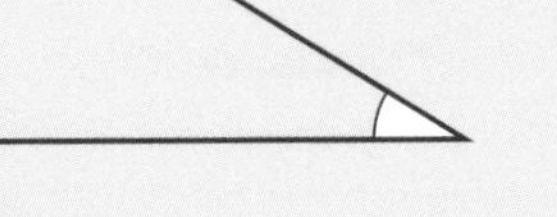

3.

b) Estimate these angles:

1.

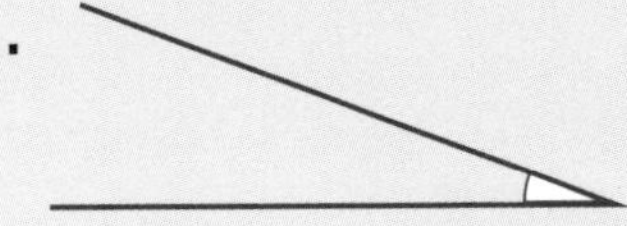

2.

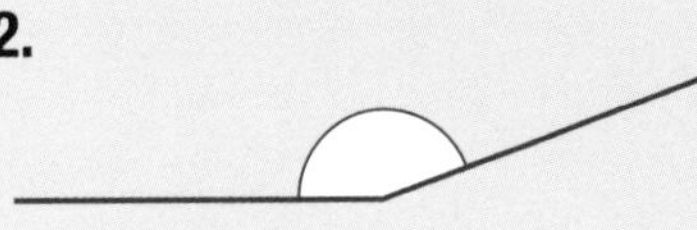

3.

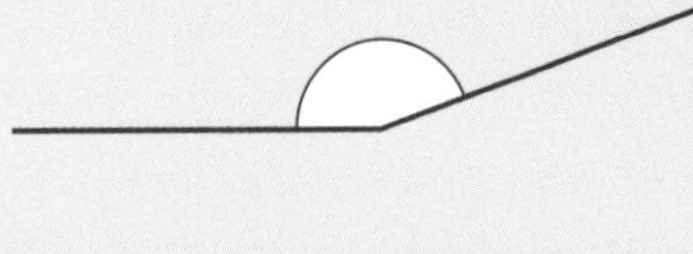

c) Measure these angles:

1.

2.

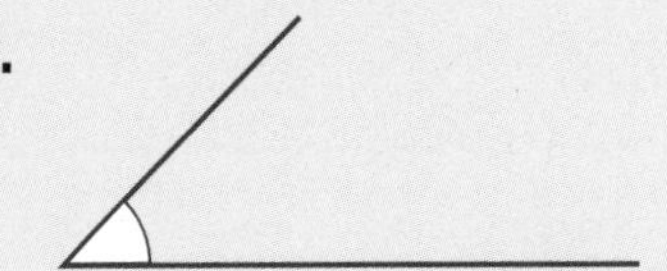

3.

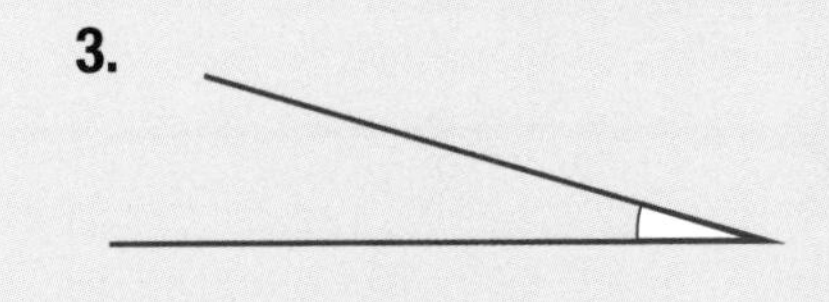

a) Estimate these angles:

1.

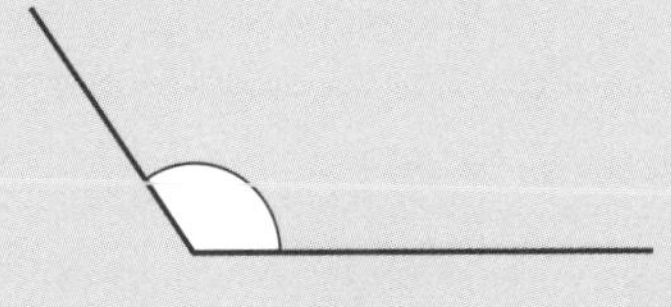

2.

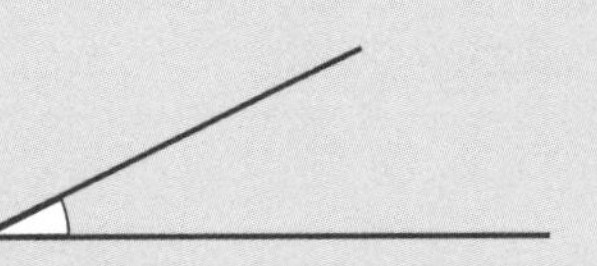

3.

b) Measure these angles:

1.

2.

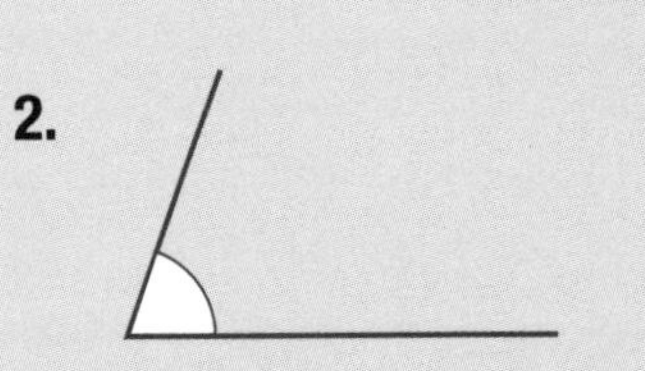

3.

c) Draw these angles:

1. 75°
2. 120°
3. 325°
4. 150°

Angles in a straight line

Half a turn is 180 degrees.
When you draw 180° angle, it is a straight line.

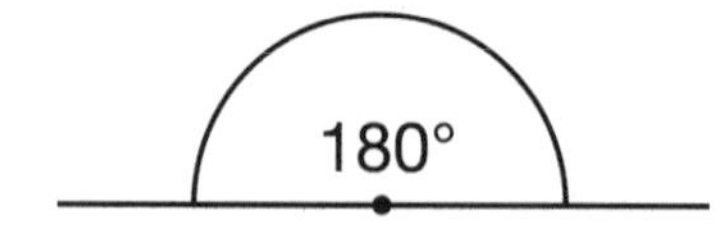

Any angles on a straight line add up to 180°.

Example

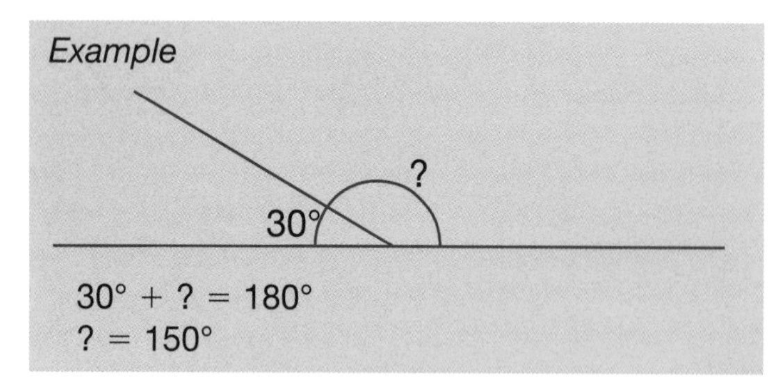

30° + ? = 180°
? = 150°

The total angles in a circle is
$2 \times 180° = 360°$.

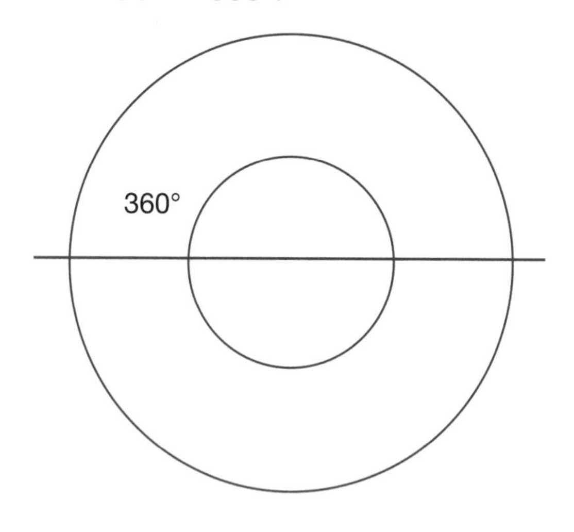

Bronze

Using the facts you have learned, work out the missing angles:

1. 70° ?
2. 40° ?
3. 65° ?
4. 115° ?
5. 150° ?
6. 165° ?
7. 175° ?
8. 20° ?

- **180° = straight line = half turn**
  360° = circle = whole turn
- **Use a protractor to check the facts above.**

a) Using the facts you have learned, work out the missing angles:

1.

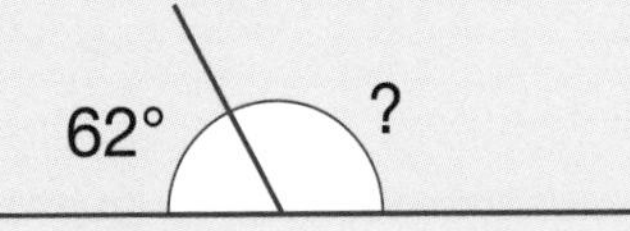

2.

3.

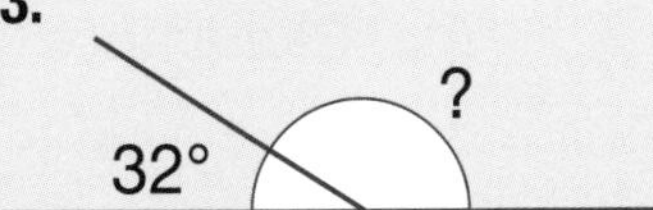

4.

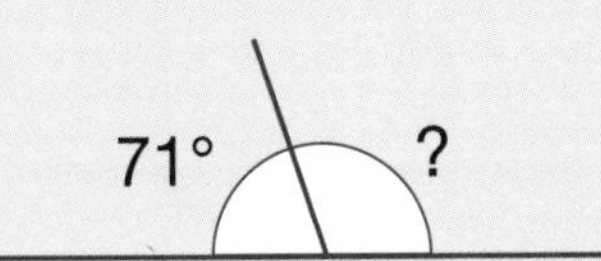

5.

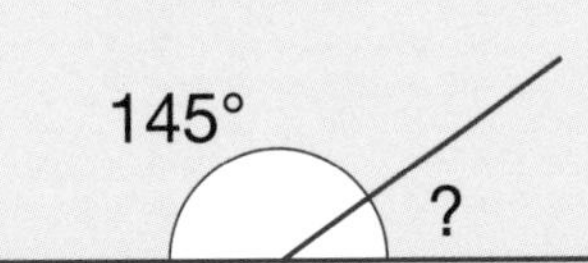

b) Now work out these:

1.

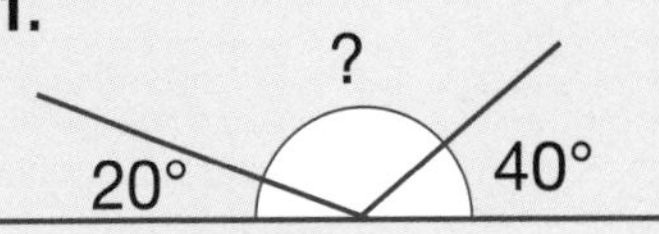

2.

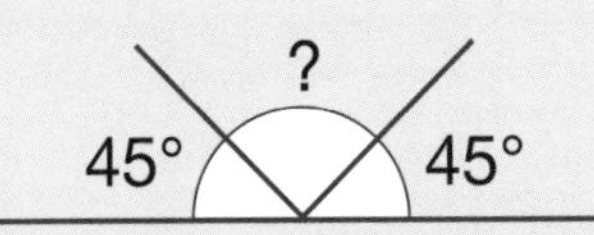

3.

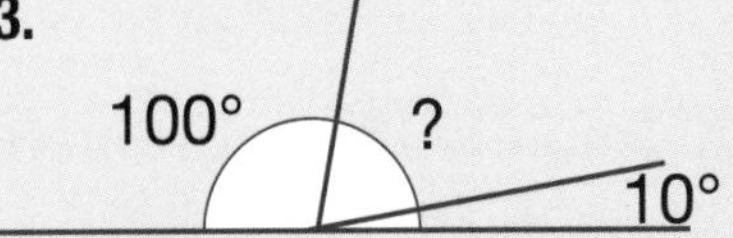

a) Find the missing angles:

1.

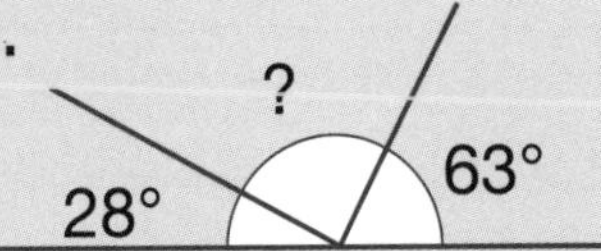

2.

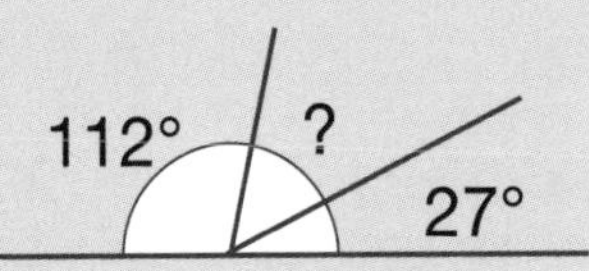

3.

b) Find the missing angles:

1.

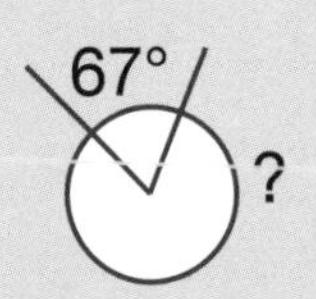

2.

3.

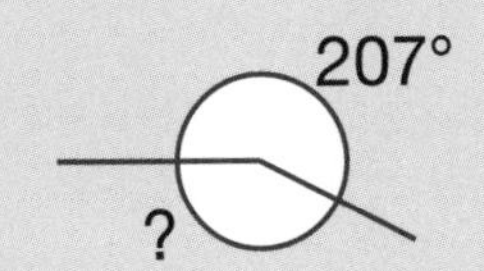

c) Find the missing angles:

1.

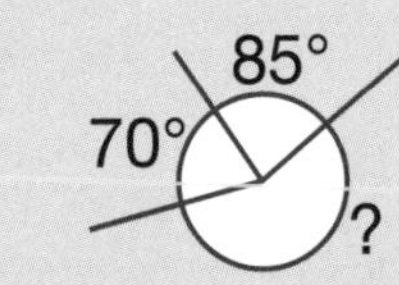

2.

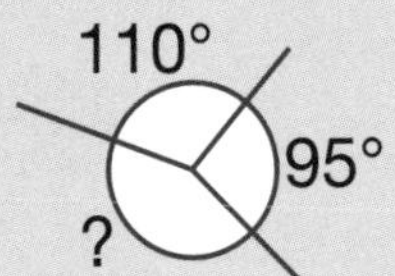

3.

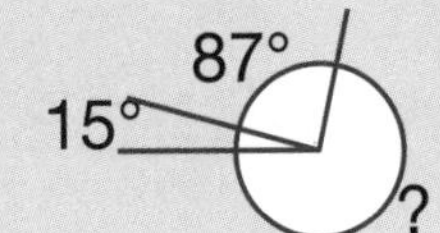

Coordinates

Coordinates give you a position on a grid.

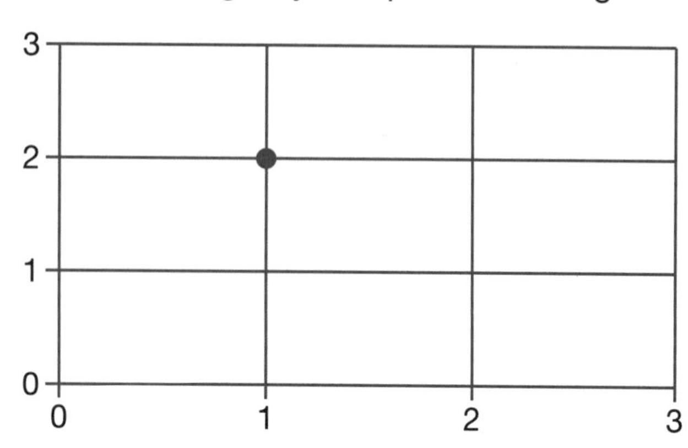

The position of the dot is (1, 2). 1 along and 2 up.

Remember to go → (along the corridor) and ↑ (up the stairs).

Complete the coordinates of each point on the picture:

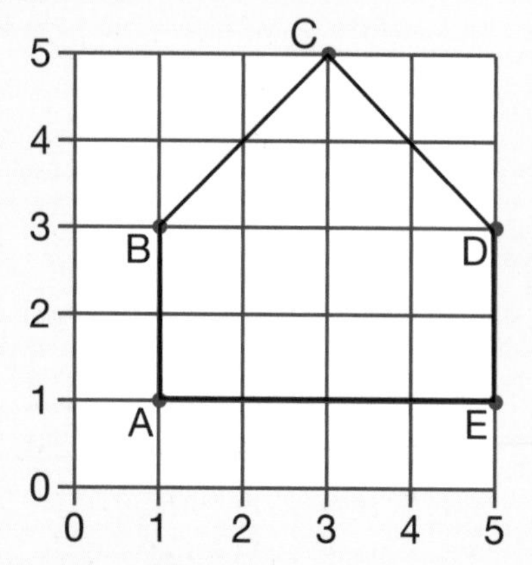

1. A = (1,)
2. B = (1,)
3. C = (3,)
4. D = (, 3)
5. E = (, 1)

Look at this grid. Write down the coordinates of each point:

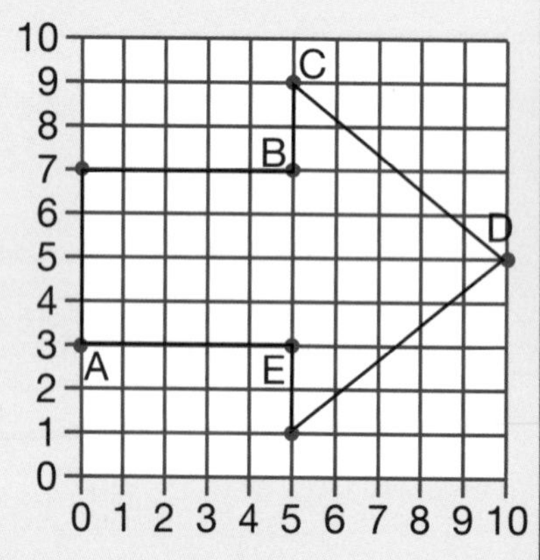

1. A =
2. B =
3. C =
4. D =
5. E =

Draw this grid in your book:

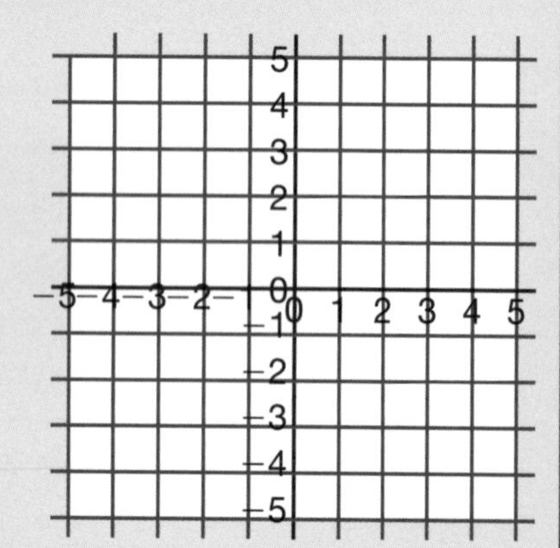

Now plot these points on the grid:

1. (2,2), (2,5), (5,5), (5,2)
2. (−2,2), (−4,2), (−3,4)
3. (−2,−2), (−4,−2), (−5,−4), (−3,−5), (−1,−4)
4. (1,−2), (1,−5), (2,−5), (2,−2)
5. Name these shapes.

Training Tips

- You say one axis or two axes. (0, 0) is called the origin.

Number puzzles

Using the clues you are given, you need to find each mystery number.

Example	My number is less than 10.	It could be 0, 1, 2, 3, 4, 5, 6, 7, 8 or 9.
	My number is odd.	It could be 1, 3, 5, 7 or 9.
	It is divisible by 3.	It could be 3 or 9.
	It is a square number.	Answer = 9

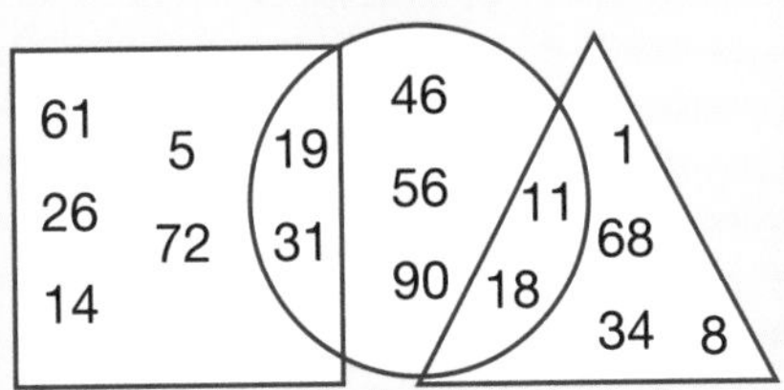

1. My number is inside the circle and inside the triangle. It is odd.
2. My number is inside the square but not inside the circle. It can be divided by 7 without a remainder.
3. My number is in the circle and inside the square. It is greater than 20.
4. My number is even. It is inside the triangle. It can be divided exactly by 6.

Who am I?

1. I have two digits. I am an even number. One of my digits is 2. The sum of my digits is 7.
2. I have two digits. I am greater than 60. I can be divided exactly by 5 and by 7.
3. I have two digits. I am a square number. I am a multiple of 5.
4. I have two digits and I am between 10 and 20. I am a multiple of 3 and the sum of my digits is 3.

Who am I?

1. I am less than 500. I am divisible by 11 and 5. I have three digits. The sum of my digits is 14.
2. I am a four-digit number. I am less than 4900 but more than 3600. I am a square number. I am a multiple of 25 and 5.
3. I am a two-digit odd number less than 100. I am a square number and the sum of my digits is 9.
4. I am the smallest number that leaves a remainder of 3 when divided by 7.

- **Write down all the possible numbers to help.**
- **Square number = a number multliplied by itself**

Word problems

Solve these word problems.

1. Read the question carefully.
2. Decide which operation to use.
3. Calculate the answer.
4. Make sure the answer makes sense.

1. Sam has 6 sweets and Rob has 5 sweets. How many sweets do they have altogether?
2. I have £12. I am given another £5. How much do I have?
3. 8 people are on a bus. 6 get off. How many people are on the bus now?
4. You have 60 litres of water. How many 10-litre buckets of water can you fill?
5. I think of a number and then divide it by 2. The answer is 15. What was my number?
6. A 100 cm tape measure is cut in half. How long is one half?

- **Drawing pictures can help or try imagining the problem.**

1. Zafar has £6.40. His sister has £4.25. How much more money does he have than his sister?
2. 15 girls and 22 boys from Year 5 are going on a trip to the zoo. The journey by bus will take 23 minutes. How many children's tickets for the bus must the school buy?
3. Matt has 25 lollipops. He has 6 people to his party. He wants to give each person 5 lollipops. Does he have enough lollipops?
4. Chad's mum has cooked 16 sausages. How many children can have 2 each?
5. There are 9 cakes on a tray. If one falls on the floor and is thrown away, how many can Sarah and Pete have each?

1. There are four CD racks. Two of the racks hold 30 CDs and two of the racks hold 45 CDs. How many CDs are there altogether in the racks?
2. Pop Flops played two concerts in August at Wembley Arena. 8120 people came to the first concert and 7845 came to the second concert. How many more people were there at the first concert?
3. I think of a number and then divide it by 12. The answer is 6. What was my number?
4. Swimming in a local swimming pool costs £3 for the first hour and £1.50 for every hour after that. How much will it cost for two people to swim for 3 hours?
5. Unleaded petrol costs 75.4p per litre. I put 40 litres in my car. How much do I have to pay?

Puzzles

Maths can be fun! Use all your maths knowledge to solve these puzzles.

Complete this magic square. All the rows, columns and diagonals must add up to the target number. The target number is 15.

	7	
9	5	
4		

Complete this magic square. All the rows, columns and diagonals must add up to the target number. The target number is 65.

17		1		15
23	5		14	
4		13	20	22
	12	19		3
11	18	25		9

Complete this magic square with the numbers 1 to 16. All the rows, columns and diagonals must add up to the target number. The target number is 34.

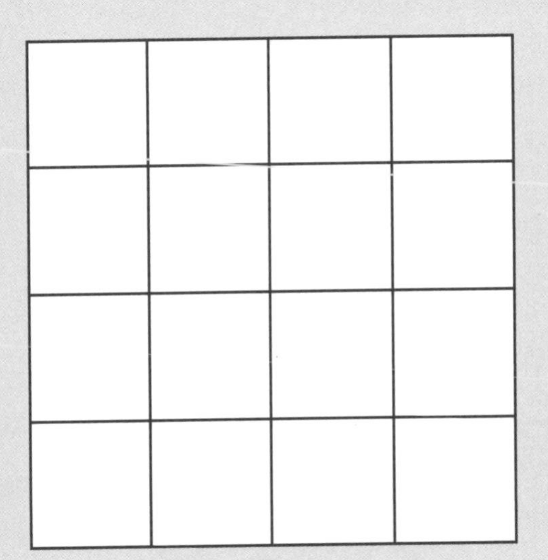

- If you are stuck, try to solve a different answer first.

Line graphs

Line graphs represent data.

The line graph below shows the change in CD-ROM sales over a year.

We can see that in February the CD-ROM sales were 24 500 and that in June they were 27 500.

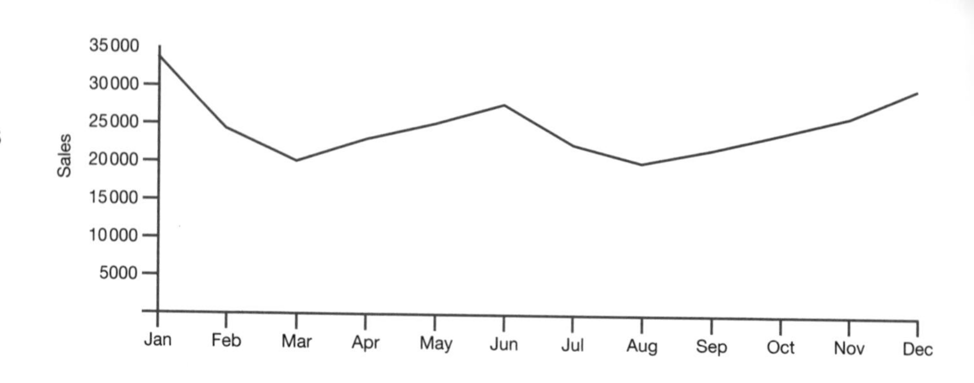

Bronze

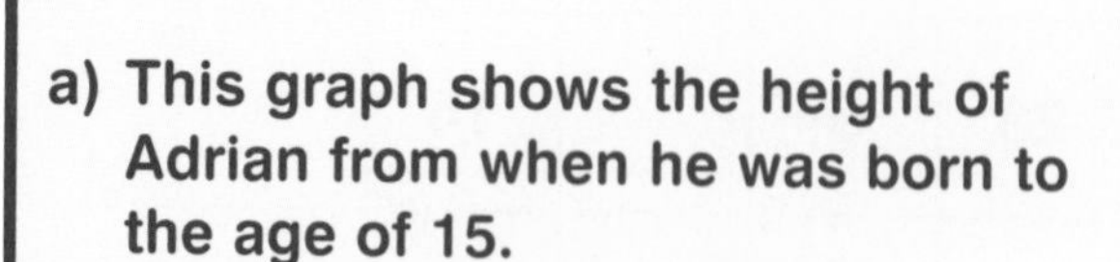

a) This graph shows the height of Adrian from when he was born to the age of 15.

1. How tall was he at 8 years old?
2. How old was he when he was 127 cm tall?
3. How much did he grow between 10 and 13?
4. How tall was he at 10 years old?
5. How old was he when he was 102 cm tall?

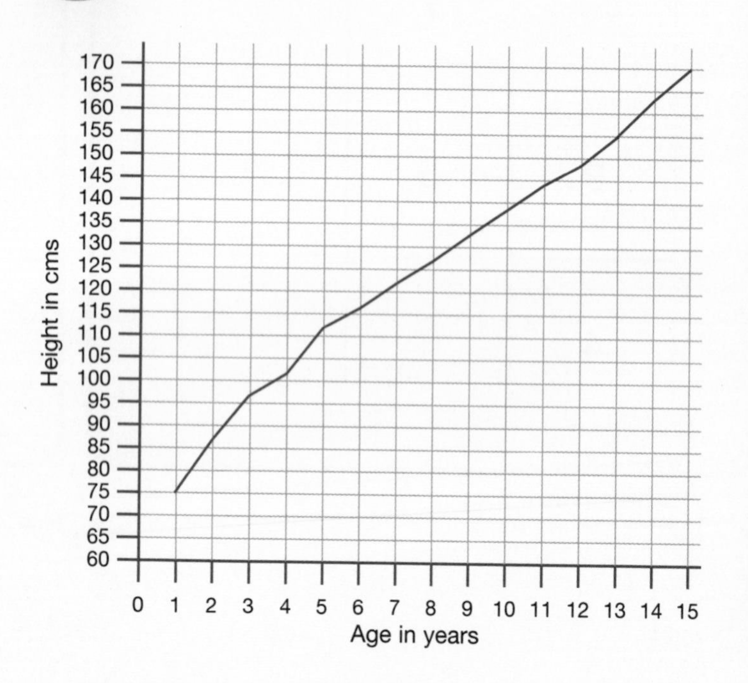

b) The data below shows the temperature in a greenhouse at different times.

9.00	10.00	11.00	12.00	1.00	2.00	3.00
8°C	12°C	18°C	20°C	16°C	12°C	6°C

Draw a line graph for the information above with a line joining the different temperatures.

- **Remember to label the axes.**
  Remember to join the points in the graph together.
- **Think about the scale to use on your graph before you start.**

Silver

a) **This line graph shows the average rainfall for each month.**

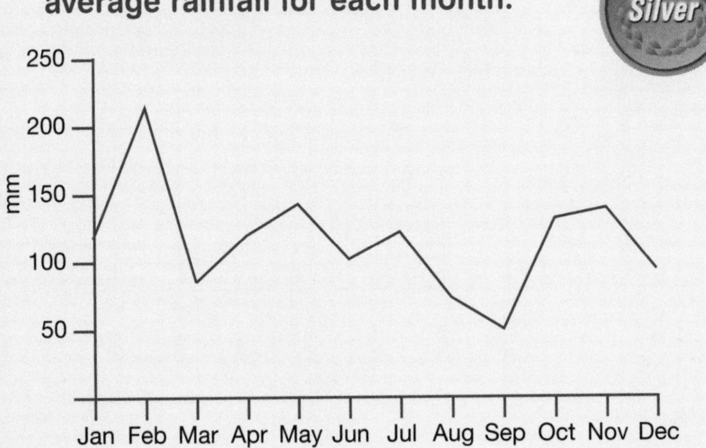

1. How much rainfall was there in March?
2. How much rainfall was there in November?
3. In which month did 101 mm of rain fall?
4. In which month did 143 mm of rain fall?
5. What was the range of rainfall?

b) **The data below shows the price of fish in a market over a year.**

Jan	Feb	Mar	Apr	May	Jun	Jul	Aug	Sept	Oct	Nov	Dec
£1.50	£1.60	£1.65	£1.55	£1.40	£1.45	£1.40	£1.50	£1.65	£1.70	£1.80	£1.75

Draw a line graph for the information above with a line joining the different prices.

Gold

a) **This line graph shows toy sales in thousands of pounds from January to December.**

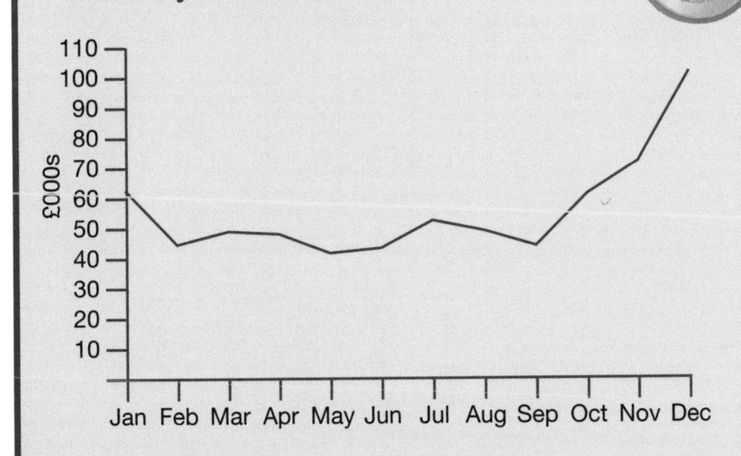

1. How much were toy sales in January?
2. How much were toy sales in November?
3. In which month were £52 500 of toys sold?
4. In which month were £101 500 of toys sold?
5. What was the range of toy sales over the year?

b) **The data below shows the movement in the price of a sports car.**

1990	1991	1992	1993	1994	1995	1996	1997
£35 500	£36 250	£36 000	£36 500	£36 500	£36 250	£36 750	£36 500

Draw a line graph for the information above with a line joining the different prices.

Bar charts and bar line charts

Bar chart

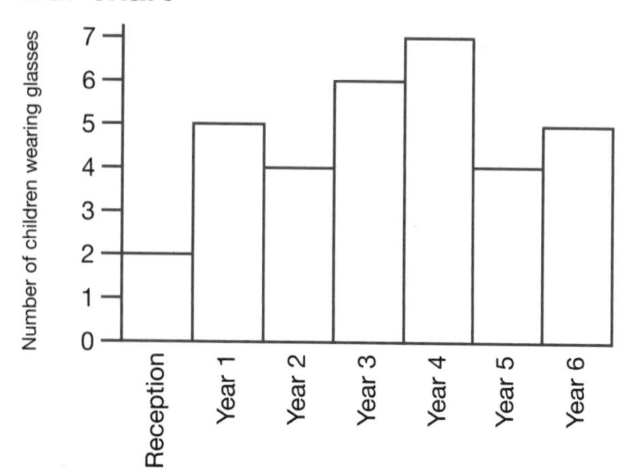

Bar line chart

Number of children having dinners

0 2 4 6 8 10 12 14 16

Reception Year 1 Year 2 Year 3 Year 4 Year 5 Year 6

Both these charts are ways of representing data.

Range

The range is the difference between the greatest and the least values.

If a scale goes from 1 to 7, range $= 7 - 1 = 6$

Mode

The mode is the most common value – the item that appears most often.
We can also call this the modal value.

This bar chart shows the number of children in 5T who had school lunch.

1. On which day did the largest number of children have school lunch?
2. On which day did the fewest children have school lunch?
3. On which days did more than 16 children have school lunch?
4. On which days did less than 16 children have school lunch?

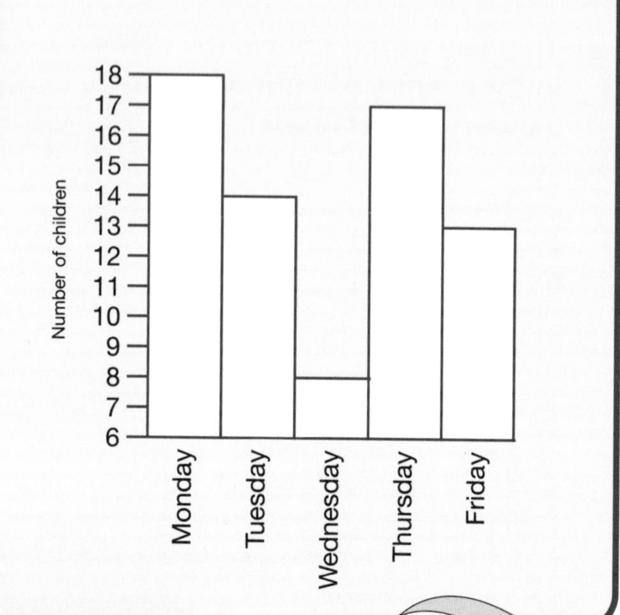

- **Learn what mode and range mean.**
- **Check the scale – does it go up in 2s, 5s, 10s or something else?**

a) Ben is raising money for charity. This bar line chart shows how much he raised each day this week.

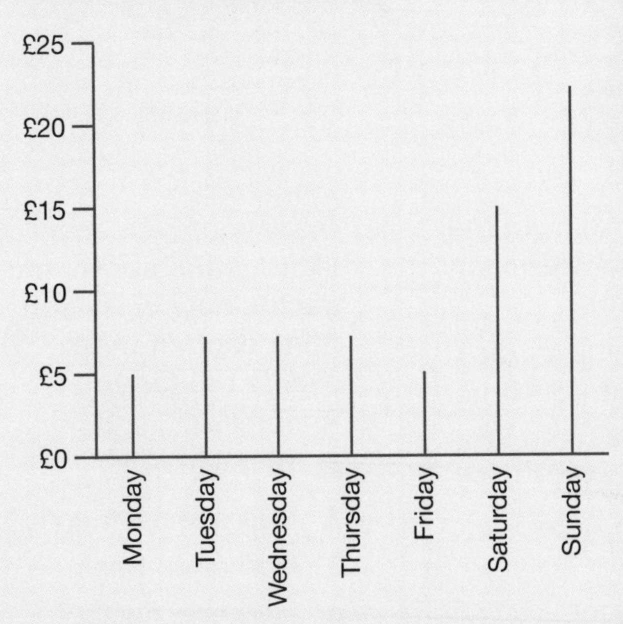

1. How much did he raise each day?
2. What was Ben's modal amount of money?
3. What was the total amount he raised?
4. What was the range of money he collected?

b) Look at the amount of goals scored by these school football teams:

Churchfields	16	Hollowbank	9
Tilebrook	16	Swallowfield	5
Littlehill	18	Rookbank	16

1. What was the modal score?
2. What was the range of scores?
3. Draw a bar chart for these results.

a) This bar chart shows the height of seven children in 5P.

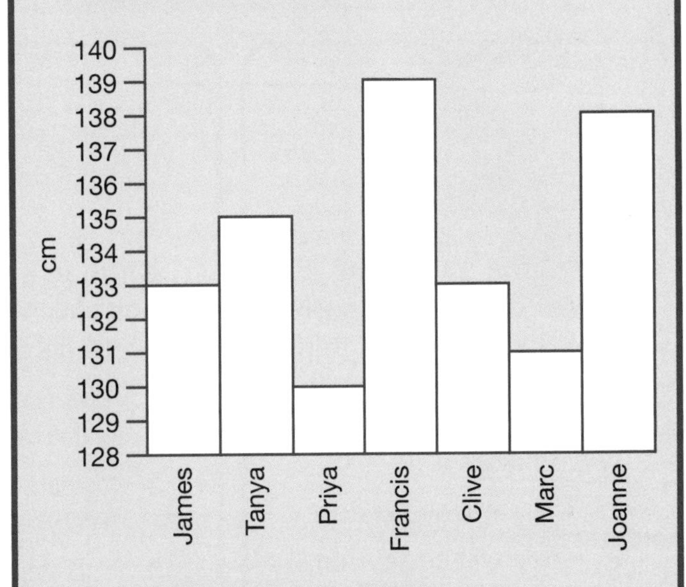

1. How tall is each child?
2. What is the modal height?
3. What is the range of heights?
4. How much taller is Tanya than Priya?

b) This data shows the amount of children who had packed lunch at Haverhill Primary School.

Mon	Tues	Wed	Thurs	Fri
98	9	16	5	16

1. Draw the bar line graph to show this information.
2. What is the modal number of packed lunches?
3. How many more children had packed lunch on Monday than Thursday?

Probability

Probability tells you how likely it is that something is going to happen.

We can use these words to describe how likely something is:

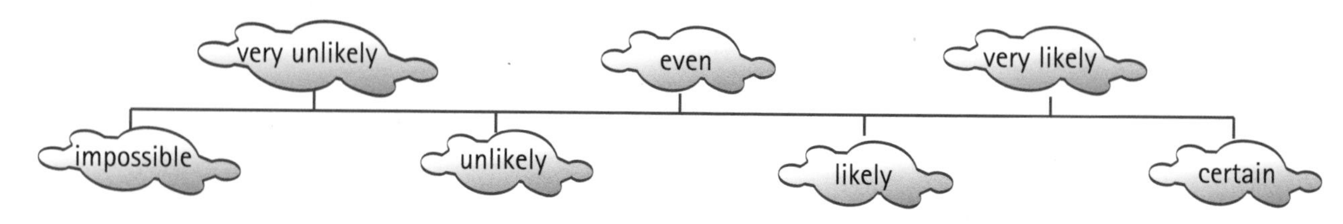

a) **It is June and Class 5D go for a walk in a park. How likely do you think each event below will be? Choose from the words above.**

1. They will see a dog
2. They will see a tree
3. They will find £100
4. Someone in 5T will fly past them

b) **Decide which shape is more likely to be picked out from each of these bags:**

1.

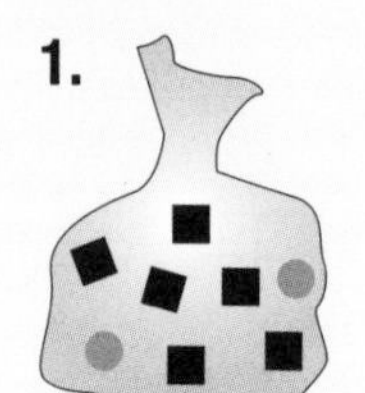

2.

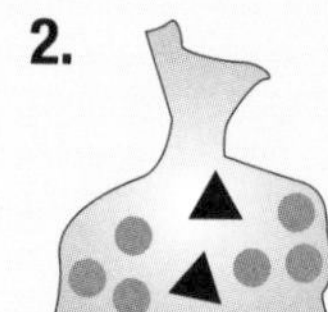

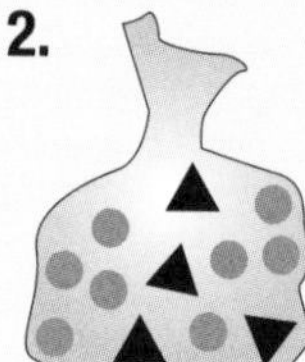

a) **Choose a word from the bubbles to go with each of these events:**

1. The first throw of dice will give a 1
2. It will snow some time this week
3. You will go to bed tonight
4. You will become a doctor when you grow up

b) **Place these events on the probability scale above.**

1. I will go to the Sun one day
2. I am 9 years old
3. I can talk
4. The Sun will rise tomorrow

a) **Draw your own scale like the one above and decide how likely you think each of these events are for you tomorrow:**

1. I will watch TV
2. I will see my friends
3. I will go to Spain
4. I will play outside

b) **List all the numbers this spinner can show if it lands on:**

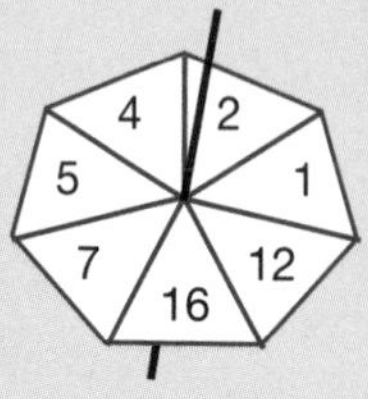

1. a number less than 4
2. a factor of 24
3. an even number
4. a multiple of 4

- **Impossible – there is no chance of it happening.**
- **Certain – it will definitely happen.**
- **50:50 – even chance.**